NEW UNDERSTANDING SCIENCE

3

NEW UNDERSTANDING SCIENCE

3

REVISED

NATIONAL

CURRICULUM

EDITION

**JOE
BOYD**
St Augustine's High School,
Edinburgh

**WALTER
WHITELAW**
Science and Technology Adviser,
City of Edinburgh Council

JOHN MURRAY

© Joe Boyd and Walter Whitelaw 1991, 1997

First published in 1991
by John Murray (Publishers) Ltd
50 Albemarle Street
London W1X 4BD

Reprinted 1991, 1992, 1995
Second edition 1997

Layouts by Fiona Webb.
Cartoons by Ainslie MacLeod and David Farris.
Illustrations by Jeff Edwards, Peter Bull Art Studio and Philip Ford.

Typeset in 11.5/13pt Futura Book by Wearset, Boldon, Tyne and Wear.
Printed and bound by Canale, Italy.

A CIP catalogue record for this book is available from the British Library.

ISBN 0 7195 7290 8

Contents

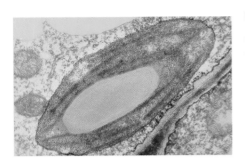
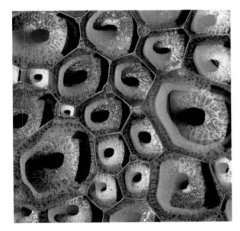
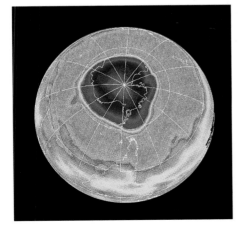

CONTENTS

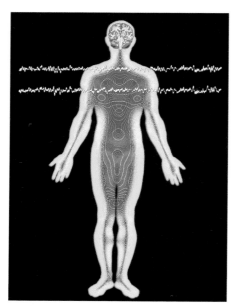

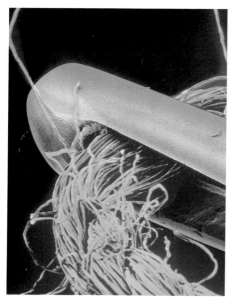

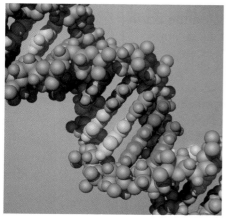

Extensions

Acknowledgements

The article on pages 98–100 is ©The Guardian and is reproduced with permission.
Some material in Unit 2 has been reused from the previous edition and was written by Peter Warren.

Explanation of photos on the opening pages of:

Unit 1 – False-colour transmission electron micrograph of a chloroplast in a leaf cell of the garden pea. In its centre is a starch granule (coloured blue); **Unit 2** – Layer of bubbles on water produced by washing-up liquid. The colours, produced just before the bubbles burst, are due to light interference; **Unit 3** – Satellite map showing a severe depletion or 'hole' in the ozone layer over Antarctica on 3 October 1990; **Unit 4** – Abstract computer artwork of a standing male figure with a healthy human brain, and spiked EEG (electroencephalogram); **Unit 5** – Coloured scanning electron micrograph of the eye of a needle, threaded with red cotton. The cotton appears as a bundle of fibres, some of which have bunched up and become tangled; **Unit 6** – Computer representation of a segment of the molecule deoxyribonucleic acid (DNA), showing the pairing of nucleotide bases; **Extensions** – Filtered photograph of light emerging from a bundle of optical fibres. The fibres are made from a special glass, which is flexible and has a high refractive index.

The following have provided photographs or given permission for photographs to be reproduced:

Cover ZEFA. **p.v** t & c Dr Jeremy Burgess/Science Photo Library, b NASA/Science Photo Library; **p.vi** t Scott Camazine/Science Photo Library, c Biophoto Associates/Science Photo Library, b Ken Eward/Science Photo Library; **p.vii** Alfred Pasieka/Science Photo Library; **p.1** Dr Jeremy Burgess/Science Photo Library; **p.5** l Rosemary Mayer/Holt Studios, tc Inga Spence/Holt Studios, tr & br Nigel Cattlin/Holt Studios, bc ©Horticultural Research International, Wellesbourne; **p.6** John Townson/Creation; **p.13** Kieran Murray/Ecoscene, inset Mark Boulton/ICCE; **p.15** tl ZEFA, tc E. A. Janes/NHPA, tr Massimo Borchi/Bruce Coleman, bl Ian Beames/Ecoscene, bc John Parrott/ICCE, br Nigel Cattlin/Holt Studios; **p.16** t & b inset Nigel Cattlin/Holt Studios, b Simon Grove/Ecoscene; **p.17** Dr Jeremy Burgess/Science Photo Library; **p.18** br Brian Rasic/Rex Features, all other photos Andrew Lambert; **p.20** Rex Features; **p.21** t John Townson/Creation, b Andrew Lambert; **p.24** t Nigel J. Dennis/NHPA, b Last Resort; **p.29** Professor Tony Wright, Institute of Laryngology & Otology/Science Photo Library; **p.31** tl & br RNID, tr ©BBC, bl Joint Mobility Unit/RNIB; **p.32** t Gernsheim Collection, Harry Ransom Humanities Research Center, The University of Texas at Austin, ct & cb Hulton Getty, b Science Museum/Science & Society Picture Library; **p.33** NASA/Science Photo Library; **p.34** tl Julian Baum/Science Photo Library, tr Space Telescope Science Institute/NASA/Science Photo Library, cr Luke Dodd/Science Photo Library, b The Kobal Collection; **p.35** bl Don Davis, NASA/Science Photo Library, br NASA/Science Photo Library; **p.37** tl & b Space Telescope Science Institute/NASA/Science Photo Library, tc John Sandford/Science Photo Library, tr NASA/Science Photo Library; **p.39** t Ben Osborne/Oxford Scientific Films, inset MI Walter/NHPA, cl ©Dr B. Booth/GeoScience Features, cr Doug Allan/Oxford Scientific Films, bl

GeoScience Features, br Brown/Ecoscene, **p.40** a., c., f. & h. GeoScience Features, b., d., e. & g. ©Dr B. Booth/GeoScience Features; **p.43** tl & tr ©Dr B. Booth/GeoScience Features, tc David Boag/Oxford Scientific Films, cl Jacolyn Wakeford/ICCE, c GeoScience Features, cr Last Resort, bl Brown/Ecoscene, br Richard Greenhill/S&R Greenhill Photo Library; **p.45** t Richard Packwood/Oxford Scientific Films, b ©Roger Tidman/FLPA; **p.46** Associated Press; **p.47** tl Arthus Bertrand/Science Photo Library, tr Martin Bond/Science Photo Library, bl Trebor Snook/ICCE, br David Parker/Science Photo Library; **p.48** Intelsat; **p.49** Scott Camazine/Science Photo Library; **p.50** Robert Harding Picture Library; **p.51** l Horticultural Research International, East Malling, cl Mark Boulton/ICCE, cr Barnaby's Picture Library, r D. H. Thompson/Oxford Scientific Films; **p.52** l & r Andrew Lambert; **p.53** tl Michael Mayer/Holt Studios, tc ©Sally & Richard Greenhill/S&R Greenhill Photo Library, tr E. A. Janes/NHPA, cl ©Roger Wilmshurst/FLPA, c Andrew Lambert, cr Hans Reinhard/Bruce Coleman Ltd., bl & bc Talya Baker, br John Townson/Creation; **p.55** tl, c & r ©Sally Greenhill/S&R Greenhill Photo Library, bl ZEFA; **p.63** Sim Town by Maxis ©1996; **p.64** tl James King-Holmes/Science Photo Library, tr Zeneca Plant Science, bl Hank Morgan/Science Photo Library, br James Holmes/Celltech Ltd/Science Photo Library; **p.65** l Bob Gibbons/Holt Studios, r Nigel Cattlin/Holt Studios; **p.66** t Roslin Institute (Edinburgh), b Henry Ausloos/NHPA; **p.67** Biophoto Associates/Science Photo Library; **p.68** l Philippe Plailly/Science Photo Library, r ©Mark Newman/FLPA; **p.72** l, c & r Andrew Lambert; **p.76** t Andrew Lambert, bl photograph with permission of ICI Chemicals & Polymers Ltd, Runcorn Site, bc Richard Glover/Ecoscene, br ©Sylvia Yorath/ICCE; **p.79** tl, tr & br Andrew Lambert, bl Last Resort; **p.80** l Last Resort, r ©R. Sheridan/Ancient Art & Architecture Collection; **p.82** NRM/Science & Society Picture Library; **p.83** Ken Eward/Science Photo Library; **p.84** Biophoto Associates/Science Photo Library; **p.86** Hulton Getty; **p.87** l Cystic Fibrosis Trust (Registered Charity 281287), c The Haemophilia Society, r Sickle Cell Society; **p.90** all photos Andrew Lambert; **p.91** all photos John Townson/Creation; **p.95** l John Mead/Science Photo Library, r Hank Morgan/Science Photo Library; **p.97** l CNRI/Science Photo Library, tr Martin Bond/Science Photo Library, br Ginies/SIPA/Rex Features; **p.98** Chris Butler/Science Photo Library; **p.100** Philippe Plailly/Eurelios/Science Photo Library; **p.101** Alfred Pasieka/Science Photo Library; **p.105** tl & bl Nigel Cattlin/Holt Studios, c Heather Angel, r ©M. Rose/FLPA; **p.106** tl Prof Stewart Lowther/Science Photo Library, tr Henk Merjenburgh/Environmental Images, bl Gary Braasch/Woodfin Camp/Colorific, br Daniel J. Cox/Oxford Scientific Films; **p.107** Richard Wehr/Custom Medical Stock Photo/Science Photo Library; **p.110** Des Jenson/Rex Features; **p.111** tl A. N.T./NHPA, tr Stephen Dalton/NHPA, bl Tsuneo Nakamura/NHPA, br Tom McHugh, Photo Researchers Inc./Oxford Scientific Films; **p.112** t Kim Gordon/Science Photo Library, b Dr Rudolph Schild/Science Photo Library; **p.114** tl P. H. & S. L. Ward/Natural Science Photos, tr GeoScience Features, bl ©Dr B. Booth/GeoScience Features, br ©B. Crisp/Ancient Art & Architecture Collection; **p.115** l IWASA/Rex Features, r ©H.A.N.A./GeoScience Features; **p.117** t & b Andrew Lambert; **p.118** t Andrew Syred/Science Photo Library, bl & br CNRI/Science Photo Library; **p.127** l & c Nigel Cattlin/Holt Studios, r Ian Beames/Ecoscene.

Introduction

Making your own notes

Why?
Note making is different from note taking. When you do something active, like write your own version of some text, you have to think about the information you are writing down. This helps you to understand and remember your work.

Where?
Your notes should be recorded in a book. They should also read like a book. Be proud of this book. It should be neat and tidy and colourful. You should be eager to show it off at science open evenings or to have it discussed at parent/guardian meetings.

How?
1 Most topics have note-making guides or key points.
2 Read the text keeping the key points in mind.
3 Include all the key points in your notes.
4 Use drawings and labelled diagrams to help you explain complicated ideas and procedures.
5 Always use your own words to describe and explain something.
6 Ask your teacher whether to use complete sentences or short phrases in your notes. You can also use spider diagrams and tables to summarise information.
7 Keep your notes short, certainly shorter than the original printed text.

And then?
Use your notes to learn from. It is a good idea to read over notes and expand them soon after the lesson. Also, use them as part of a regular revision plan.

An example?
The diagram on the left gives an example of notes that have been made from page 2 of this book.

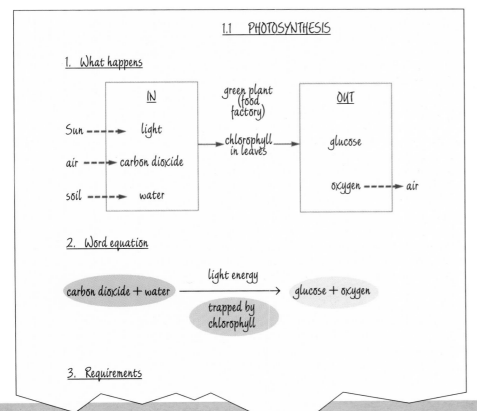

Spaceship Earth

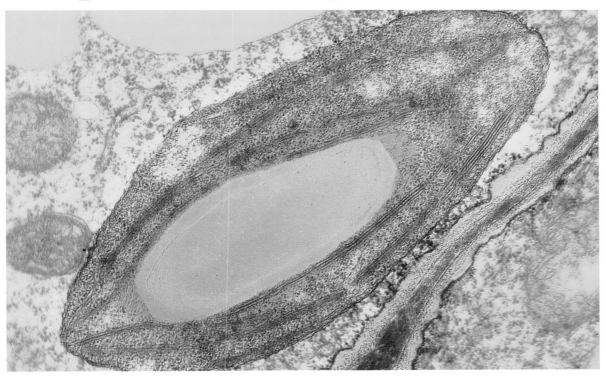

BIG IDEAS IN THIS UNIT

1 Green plants do not get food from the soil. They make their own food by the process of photosynthesis.

2 In photosynthesis energy from the Sun is used to change carbon dioxide and water into glucose and oxygen.

3 Plants carry out aerobic respiration all day and all night to release energy from the food they make.

4 Plant roots absorb essential minerals and elements, such as nitrogen, for healthy growth.

5 A pyramid of numbers is one way of indicating the number of organisms at each link in a food chain.

6 Poisonous chemicals accumulate in food chains.

7 A food web is made up of the many linked food chains in a habitat.

1.1 *Photosynthesis*

A Plant factories

If you were sent into space you would need food and oxygen to survive. You would have to be sure that these would never run out. You would also need to be sure that your artificial environment was kept in perfect balance.

Planet Earth *is* a spaceship orbiting the Sun. On the whole the environment *is* kept in balance. One group of living things is mostly responsible for this. This group is green plants. Green plants are food factories. They are able to change raw materials into useful products by capturing and using energy from the Sun in a process called **photosynthesis**.

Plants cannot use the Sun as a direct energy source for growth. Instead they capture the light energy using a green **pigment** (colouring) called **chlorophyll** in leaf cells.

The energy is used to change the raw materials into products. This is just like a plastics factory where the raw material from oil is changed into a product – plastics – using energy.

There are two raw materials for photosynthesis

- the gas **carbon dioxide**, which plants take from the air through their leaves
- **water**, which plants take from the soil through their roots. The soil does *not* supply food to the plant.

The products of photosynthesis are glucose (a simple sugar) and oxygen gas

- **glucose** is used by the plant as a food source, providing energy for growth and repair. Some glucose is changed into starch and stored for later use. Some is changed into more complex plant building compounds
- **oxygen** is released into the air from the leaves.

The process of photosynthesis involves many chemical reactions. However, it is possible to write a summary word equation to show what happens.

$$\text{carbon dioxide} + \text{water} \xrightarrow[\text{trapped by }\textbf{chlorophyll}]{\textbf{light energy}} \text{glucose} + \text{oxygen}$$

So, through photosynthesis, green plants provide food and oxygen for all other living things. Where would spaceship Earth be without them?

water from stem

carbon dioxide from the air

water moves up the stem

water from the soil

Collect

- Balloon sheet

Gases have weight

It is quite hard to believe that a wooden door that you can knock on, or a heavy wooden log that you can try to lift are made mostly from the elements carbon and oxygen. These come from the gas carbon dioxide.

Watch your teacher demonstrate that gases have weight by weighing empty balloons and then balloons filled with various gases.

Collect

- 1 g of mustard seeds
- 100 cm³ beaker
- Filter paper
- Distilled water
- Cling film
- Dropper
- Electronic balance

Plants and soil

Plants do not get food from the soil. This experiment, if carried out very accurately, will provide evidence of this. Work in pairs or fours.

1 Accurately weigh

- the mustard seeds
- one sheet of dry filter paper.

Keep an accurate record.

2 Soak the filter paper in distilled (pure) water. Squeeze out any excess water. Fold it to fit in the beaker but do not put it in the beaker yet.

3 Spread the seeds evenly over the surface of the filter paper. Weigh this. Keep an accurate record. Put the paper in the beaker and cover the top with cling film.

4 Each time you have a science lesson carefully mop up any condensation on the glass or cling film with the filter paper.

5 When the mustard plants have had two green leaves for several days

- mop up any condensation (as before)
- weigh the filter paper and mustard plants together.

Keep a record. Compare this with the starting weights.

6 Carefully remove the plants from the filter paper. Weigh these. Dry the filter paper and re-weigh it. Compare these weights with the starting weights.

While you are setting up your experiments your teacher will 'plant' some seeds on filter paper and in compost.

Collect

- Starch test sheet
- Alcohol
- Bunsen burner
- Tripod
- Mat
- Beaker
- Test tube and rack
- Forceps
- White tile
- Iodine solution
- Report sheet
- Summary sheet

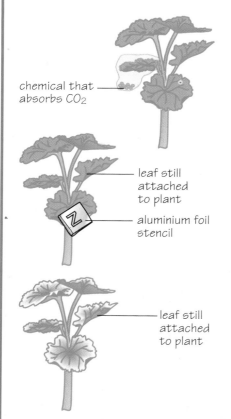

chemical that absorbs CO_2

leaf still attached to plant

aluminium foil stencil

leaf still attached to plant

Raw materials for photosynthesis

If any one of the raw materials required for photosynthesis is missing the process will not take place.

Plants change the glucose made by photosynthesis into starch. So if a plant leaf contains starch it is an indication that photosynthesis has taken place. Your teacher will demonstrate how to test a green leaf for the presence of starch.

Your task is to show that plants do need the raw materials carbon dioxide, light energy and the light-energy-capture system – the green pigment chlorophyll – to carry out photosynthesis.

Your teacher will put you in a group and ask you to carry out one experiment. The plants you will use in the experiments will have all been kept in the dark for a few days so that they have used up any store of starch before the experiments begin.

1 Do plants need carbon dioxide for photosynthesis?

Some of the leaves on the plant in this experiment are sealed in a polythene bag containing a chemical that absorbs carbon dioxide from the air.

Find out where the starch is.

2 Do plants need light for photosynthesis?

Some of the leaves on the plant in this experiment have been covered with stencils.

Find out where the starch is.

3 Do plants need chlorophyll for photosynthesis?

The leaves on the plant in this experiment have white areas where there is no chlorophyll.

Find out where the starch is.

When you have completed your task collect a report sheet. As a group prepare a report to present to the rest of the class on your experiment. You must

- state the aim of your experiment
- describe how the plant was treated before you tested it
- describe the test you did and the results
- **explain** the result
- state a conclusion.

Take part in the group presentations. Listen carefully to what the other groups say about their experiments. Discuss the results and when you are sure you understand the experiments collect and complete the photosynthesis summary sheet.

Write the title *Photosynthesis* in your book. Make notes including these key points

- What happens in photosynthesis
- A word equation for photosynthesis
  (Show the raw materials in red, the products in blue and the energy-trapping system in green.)
- The requirements for photosynthesis.
  (Stick your photosynthesis summary sheet into your book here.)

Write the title *Soil is not a food source for plants* in your book. Use the results of your mustard seed experiment to explain how you know that plants do not get food from the soil they grow in.

B Making the most of photosynthesis

The photographs below show how humans try to improve the growth of plants by providing the best possible conditions for photosynthesis.

Irrigation (above and right)

Warm conditions

Extra carbon dioxide

Constant light

Explain how each of the situations shown provides good conditions for photosynthesis.

1.2 Growing plants

A Essential elements

You need food in the form of carbohydrate, fat and protein for energy, growth and repair. You also need minerals and vitamins for general good health.

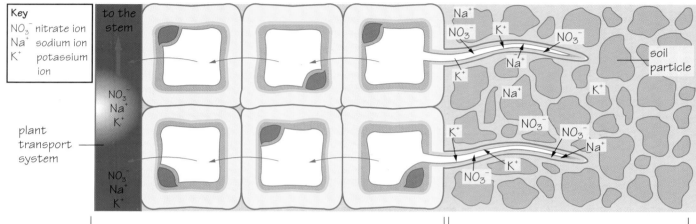

Key
NO_3^- nitrate ion
Na^+ sodium ion
K^+ potassium ion

to the stem

plant transport system

soil particle

— cross section of part of plant root in the soil — — soil with minerals dissolved in soil water —

The same is true for plants. Photosynthesis provides plants with food in the form of glucose for energy, growth and repair. Glucose provides the elements carbon, hydrogen and oxygen.

Plants also need other elements such as nitrogen, and certain metal elements, like potassium, to grow strongly. Various mineral salts in the soil provide these important elements. They are not foods because they do not provide energy to the plant.

Mineral salts are dissolved in soil water and plants take them in through root hair cells.

Collect

- Fertiliser labels
- Mustard seeds on filter paper
- Mustard seeds in compost
- Scrap paper

Fertilisers

Collect examples of plant fertiliser packs. Read the information on the packs to find out what elements the fertiliser provides. Make a list of the elements supplied and note down what these are needed for on scrap paper.

More mustard

Your teacher planted some mustard seeds on filter paper and on compost. The seeds were watered with pure, distilled water. Only the seeds in compost have the minerals needed for healthy growth.

Mustard grown on filter paper

Mustard grown in compost

Write a description of both sets of seedlings on your scrap paper.

- Plant mineral card set

Plant diets

The healthy tomato plant is shown beside unhealthy plants. Each lacks one important element for growth. A good gardener can look at an unhealthy plant and work out which element or elements are missing from its diet.

a Full diet   **b** Diet lacking nitrogen   **c** Diet lacking potassium   **d** Diet lacking phosphorus   **e** Diet lacking magnesium

1 Discuss the appearance of each plant. Decide why each element is important. Write your ideas down on scrap paper.
2 Collect a plant mineral card set. Complete each card to show what elements should be added to the plant's diet.

Write the title *What plants need for healthy growth* in your book. Use the information on these pages and your notes on scrap paper to make notes including these key points

- Mineral salts
  (What are mineral salts? Where are they found?)
- How plants obtain mineral salts
- Why certain elements are important.
  (Stick your plant mineral card set into your book here.)

B Comparing plant and animal diets

There are similarities and differences between the diets of green plants and animals. Copy and complete the table below.

Animals	need food for energy	get food by eating plants or other animals	need minerals for good health	get minerals by eating plants or other animals
Green plants				

1.3 Balancing gases

A Carbon dioxide and oxygen in balance

Green plants use the glucose they produce in photosynthesis as a source of energy for growth and repair. Plants release the energy in glucose by the process of aerobic respiration (respiration needing oxygen/air), just as animals do. The word equation for aerobic respiration in plants is given below.

$$glucose + oxygen \xrightarrow{\text{respiration – releasing energy}} carbon\ dioxide + water$$

This is exactly the same equation as for photosynthesis – but in the opposite direction. Respiration releases energy from glucose. In photosynthesis light energy is transferred to glucose. The two equations can be shown together.

$$glucose + oxygen \underset{\text{photosynthesis – transferring energy}}{\overset{\text{respiration – releasing energy}}{\rightleftharpoons}} carbon\ dioxide + water$$

Plants carry out respiration all day and all night, as do animals. Photosynthesis, however, can only take place when there is light. During the day the rate (speed) of photosynthesis is greater than the rate of respiration and this can mask the fact that plants are respiring at the same time.

Daytime

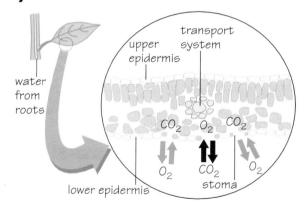

$$carbon\ dioxide + water \underset{\text{respiration}}{\overset{\text{photosynthesis}}{\rightleftharpoons}} glucose + oxygen$$

The rate of photosynthesis is greater than the rate of respiration

Night-time

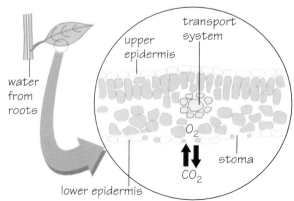

$$glucose + oxygen \xrightarrow{\text{respiration}} carbon\ dioxide + water$$

Only respiration takes place

The amount of carbon dioxide and oxygen in the air is balanced by these two important biological processes, which occur in green plants.

Write the title *Plant respiration* in your book. Make notes including these key points

- The equation for aerobic respiration
- Comparing aerobic respiration and photosynthesis.
  (You could produce a table in two columns here and compare the equations, the gaseous reactants, the gaseous products and when the processes take place.)

Collect

- 3 boiling tubes
- Pond weed
- Lamp
- Bicarbonate indicator solution
- Anything else you need
- Poster paper
- Coloured pencils
- Summary sheet

The gas carbon dioxide is removed from the air by green plants as a raw material for photosynthesis. It is passed into the air by green plants as a product of respiration.

Bicarbonate indicator solution changes colour when carbon dioxide is added or removed from the solution. Your teacher will show you the colour changes.

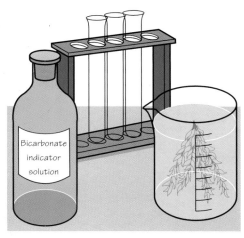

1 Work in a small team. You have to design an experiment using pond weed and bicarbonate indicator in boiling tubes so that

- in one boiling tube the bicarbonate indicator goes yellow
- in one boiling tube the bicarbonate indicator goes purple
- in one boiling tube the bicarbonate indicator does not change colour.

2 Think about *why* and *when* the indicator will change colour. Decide which variable to alter, and which variables to keep constant. In the right conditions you will see a colour change in 20 minutes.

 1 Collect some poster paper. In a group make a mini-poster using diagrams to **describe** and **explain** your results. Present your ideas to the rest of the class. Listen to other groups' ideas.
2 Collect and complete a summary sheet. Stick this into your book.

B Say it with flowers

If you are in hospital feeling unwell it's nice to get visitors. They may bring plants or flowers to cheer you up.

Usually plants are kept in hospital wards during the daytime but removed at night for the sake of patients' health.

Write a note to pin on the nurses' and doctors' notice-board explaining why it is hospital policy to remove plants from the wards at night.

1.4 Energy chains

A Pyramids of numbers

The flow of energy through an ecosystem begins when green plants trap light energy from the Sun in photosynthesis. Plants grow and increase in mass. This **biomass**, produced as a result of photosynthesis, provides food for animals. Energy is transferred along a food chain first when plants are eaten by animals, then when those animals are eaten by other animals.

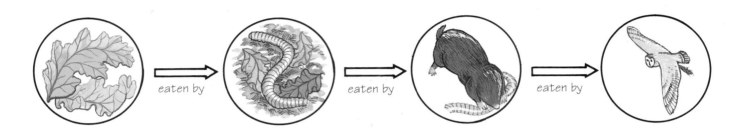

eaten by   eaten by   eaten by

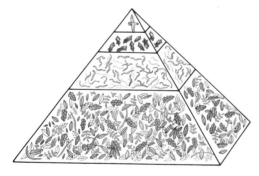

The mole shown in the food chain above eats a lot of food in one month – perhaps 1500 g of worms – but most of this is not changed into biomass (body tissue). If it were the mole would soon be as big as you are. At best about 10% of food is used for growth. Most of it is broken down by respiration to provide energy for growth, movement and body heat, and any indigestible food is **egested** (expelled) as waste. So there have to be many more worms than moles in an ecosystem for the mole to survive. In the same way there have to be more moles than barn owls if the owls are to survive.

This **pyramid of numbers** is a way of showing these ideas. The size of each layer in the pyramid represents the **total number** of living things at that level in the food chain. The shape shows that the animal at the end of the food chain (the top of the pyramid) is supported by many more living things under it. You too are part of a pyramid of numbers. You are at the top of the pyramid (unless something eats you!).

A **pyramid of biomass** has a similar shape. But instead of the total number the size of each layer represents the **total biomass** at each level of the food chain.

A pyramid of numbers can also explain how **toxic** (poisonous) materials build up along a food chain. For example, **herbicides** (weedkillers) are sprayed on to plants. These kill some but not all plant species. The living plants absorb some of the toxins, which are very difficult for the plant to break down. When the plants are eaten by animals, they too absorb some of the toxins. An individual usually eats a large number of the organisms below it in the pyramid. Therefore at each layer of the pyramid of numbers, the level of toxins in each individual is higher. Whereas low concentrations of toxins may have little effect on a living organism, high levels of toxins reduce fertility and can even be fatal.

Collect

- An energy chain game kit
- 3 dice

Follow the instructions to play the energy chain game.

 Write the title *Energy chains* in your book. Make notes including these key points

- Food chains
- Pyramids of numbers and biomass
- How toxins build up in food chains.

B Human food chain

Collect

- A set of bathroom scales

1 Weigh yourself to the nearest kilogram.
2 For every kilogram of body mass, you need about 170 kJ of energy every day. Work out how many kilojoules of energy you need each day.

$$\text{Energy needs (}\textbf{EN}\text{)} = \text{(your mass} \times 170\,kJ\text{)}$$

3 Copy and complete the table below.
   For each food, work out how many kilograms would provide your energy needs for one day.

1 kg of this food	contains energy (E)	kg of food needed for 1 day (= EN/E)
rice	15 000 kJ	
sugar	16 500 kJ	
peanuts	24 500 kJ	

 1 a What is the energy in food used for?
   b A week's meals might contain 5 kg of food. Explain why you are not 5 kg heavier at the end of the week.
2 Write a food chain in which you provide the last link.
3 Draw your food chain from question 2 as a pyramid of numbers.

1.5 *Food webs*

A From chains to webs

In any habitat the Sun is at the start of each food chain. Most organisms are part of several food chains. Food chains are linked together in a **food web**. In a food web some organisms called **decomposers** recycle important minerals and elements by bringing about the decay of dead animals and plants. A rock pool food web is shown below.

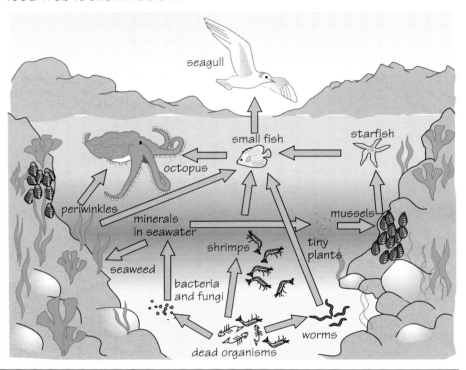

Collect

- Food web cards
- Scrap paper
- Food web board
- Wool
- Drawing pins
- Scissors
- Disaster cards
- Summary sheet

Play the food chain game in a group of four. The aims of the game are to

- build up food chains using information on the food web cards
- show how the food chains become a food web
- demonstrate how fragile the food web is using the disaster cards.

1 Deal out the food web cards.
2 Your group should make as many food chains as it can using the information on the cards. Write the food chains down on scrap paper.
3 Place the cards on the board.
4 Use wool to join the plants and animals in food chains.
5 Turn over the first disaster card. Follow the instructions.

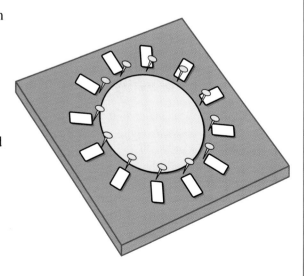

Write the title *Food webs* in your book. Make notes including these key points

- What is a food web?
- The importance of decomposers in food webs
  (Give some examples of decomposers.)
- An example of a food web
  (Make a diagram of the food web from the game here; remember to draw in the Sun and explain what the arrows represent.)
- A delicate balance.
  (Explain the effect of one disaster, from the disaster cards, on the food web.)

 Complete the summary sheet and then stick it into your book.

B Pass it on

Sometimes dangerous substances get into an ecosystem. For example, if a tanker carrying toxic chemicals sank off the shore, the rock pool food web might be affected.

 1 Make a diagram of the rock pool food web, showing the names of all the organisms present. Circle the names of all the organisms that

- carry out photosynthesis in green
- are herbivores in blue
- are omnivores in black
- are carnivores in red.

Make a colour key for your food web.
2 Describe the effect on the food web of toxic chemicals killing all the mussels in the rock pool.
3 Explain how the toxic chemicals can enter the food web from dead organisms.

1.6 *Problem*

Grow more

Many farmers and gardeners use artificial fertilisers to improve the growth of their plants.

Your problem is to investigate the most effective way to use an artificial fertiliser to improve the growth of peas. You will have to consider

- which variables you should keep constant
- what concentrations of fertiliser you will use
- what control experiment you should set up
- how you will measure and compare the growth of the peas
- the cost of the fertiliser and how to reduce any wastage.

Collect

- Fertiliser
- Peas
- Any equipment you need

Work in a group.

1 Discuss the problem and possible solutions.
2 Decide on the best solution and write down an outline plan.
3 Set up your experiment.
4 Record the growth of the peas over a week or so.

 Produce a full-page advertisement for your fertiliser (use colour, stencils etc. to make it attractive).

- Use the results of your experiments to suggest the best way of using the fertiliser.
- Give information on the cost of use, and hints on how to prevent waste.

1.7 Talkabout

Useful plants

We depend on plants for food and oxygen. But we use them for so many other things too.

Plants for fun

Plants for medicine

Plants for decoration

Plants for building

Plants for fuel

Plants for clothing

1 Work in a group of three or four. Throw a die to decide which subject you will find out about. Use books, posters and multimedia resources to find

- at least three examples of how plants are used in your subject area
- the names of the plants used and where they come from.

2 Each member of the group should neatly write out a few sentences on a piece of card or paper about one example. Every member of the class should read out their information. Use the cards to make a wall display – the cards could be the 'leaves' on a tree. Alternatively you could use the cards to prepare a database on useful plants.

1.8 *Readabout*

The artificial conditions in a greenhouse are perfect for pests such as whitefly. All natural predators are kept out. Now one form of parasitic wasp can be released into the greenhouse. The wasps reduce the whitefly population

The water hyacinth was introduced by humans to Lake Victoria in Africa. It has no native predators and now covers huge areas of the lake, upsetting the local food web. Weevils (inset) have been introduced as a natural population control

Biological control

When an ecosystem is in balance the **population** (number of individuals) of most species stays fairly constant. Within a species individuals who are well adapted will produce offspring, which are more likely to survive and pass on their successful characteristics than the offspring of less well-adapted individuals. This keeps the species strong and able to survive competition, predators and disease. If these natural controls are absent a population grows very rapidly.

We have learned how to manage our environment. For example, we grow food efficiently on farms. However, this also produces an artificial ecosystem where there may be no natural population controls. Sometimes we introduce a new species without thinking of the consequences for the native plants and animals. The new, introduced, species increases in number and may attract large numbers of pests or simply take over the environment, damaging the local food web.

It has been usual to control animal pests on food crops using chemicals called pesticides. We control plant pests (weeds!) using chemicals called herbicides. However, there are now concerns about using these chemicals. Some pesticides kill not only the pests but also the predators of pests and the bees needed to pollinate the crops. Some chemicals also build up in food chains. This reduces fertility and slowly poisons many animals. The chemicals even enter human food chains.

Nowadays, humans are turning to biological control to keep pest populations in check. This system uses natural enemies of the pest to control its population. It is not a new idea. One of the earliest recorded examples of biological control was by the Chinese, who used a particular species of ant to control leaf-eating pests in fruit orchards. Two modern day examples are shown on the left.

There are many examples of biological control. They don't all work, but there are enough success stories to encourage scientists to continue research in this area. Some other examples are control of

- the prickly pear (*Opuntia*) in Australia
- saw flies in conifer forests
- the rabbit population in Britain with myxomatosis
- cane beetle attack on sugar cane by cane toads in Australia.

1 What does biological control mean?
2 Why is biological pest control better for the environment than using chemicals?
3 Use available resources to read about one of the biological pest controls above, or you can find your own example. Write a short report on the method you choose. It can be in the form of

- a newspaper story
- a script for a science TV programme
- an interview with a farmer using the method.

2

Detecting energy

BIG IDEAS IN THIS UNIT

1 In air light travels in a straight line at a constant speed.
2 We see non-luminous objects because they reflect and scatter light into our eyes.
3 Light is bent (refracted) when it passes from one material into another.
4 White light is made up of a spectrum of colours. The colour of an object in white light depends on the colour of light reflected by the object.
5 Coloured filters transmit certain colours from white light and can alter the appearance of objects.
6 Sound waves are caused by vibrations that are transmitted through gases, liquids and solids.
7 A sound can be described by the size (amplitude) and frequency of the vibrations causing it.

2.1 *Energy sensors*

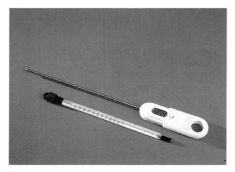

Thermometers

Thermosensor

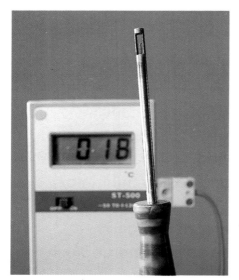

Thermocouple

A Heat, light and sound

Our bodies can detect heat, light and sound. However, we use instruments to extend the range of measurements we can make and to improve the accuracy of our measurements.

Heating is a process that transfers energy to a substance. The more energy the particles of a substance have, the faster they move and the higher the temperature becomes. Temperature is a measure of the *average energy* of these particles. The more particles there are, the more energy is required to raise the temperature by 1°C. Compare, say, heating a bath full of water with heating a kettle-full.

Our skin contains temperature-sensing nerve cells. We use thermometers, heat sensors or probes and thermocouples as temperature-measuring instruments. Thermocouples are made of two different metals joined together in a circuit. When the joins are at different temperatures a tiny current flows. The size of the current can be used as a measure of temperature.

Luminous objects produce light. The Sun is luminous and so is an electric light bulb. We see non-luminous objects, like this book, the desk, chairs and people in the room, because these objects reflect and scatter light that then enters our eyes. When we look at the Moon in the night sky we see it because it reflects sunlight from its surface back to Earth. Light can be detected using our eyes, light meters and light sensors.

Sound is made by vibrating objects. The sound waves travel as a pulse through the air. Sound can be detected by our ears, decibel meters and microphones.

Photographic light meter

Light sensor

Sound level meter

Microphone

Collect

- Range of hearing sheet
- Light meter
- Black paper
- Pin
- Thermometer
- Two beakers
- Light sensor
- Temperature sensor
- Interfacing equipment
- Computer and screen
- Warm water
- Cold water
- Iced water

Detecting sound
Your teacher will use a signal generator to produce a range of sounds from low notes to high notes. Investigate the range of hearing of humans. Collect and complete a range of hearing sheet.

Detecting light
Work in a small group. Design some simple experiments to investigate the sensitivity of the light sensor or light meter. Talk about one or two variables you want to investigate before you begin. Tell your teacher what you need.

Detecting heat
Investigate the accuracy and sensitivity of your skin as a heat detector compared with a thermometer and temperature sensor. Use tap water from the hot and cold taps only. Iced water may be available.

Think of at least two questions you want to answer in your investigation.

 Write the title *Detecting energy* in your book. Make notes including these key points

- Range of hearing
  (Describe the experiment and stick the range of hearing sheet into your book.)
- Light
  (Give a brief description of your experiments including the questions you asked and your results.)
- Heat.
  (Give a brief description of your experiments including the questions you asked and your results.)

B Detection

 Decide which of the following forms of energy you can detect

- kinetic energy (movement energy)
- nuclear energy
- electrical energy.

If you think you can detect any of these, describe how you do this.

2.2 *Light travels*

A Beams of light

If a beam of light from a laser passes through smoke or dust, you can see that the beam is perfectly straight. Light travels in straight lines at a fantastic speed – about 300 000 kilometres per second!

When an electric light is switched on or a camera flashes the light seems to enter our eyes instantly. We are too close to the light source to be aware that light travels through the air. The Sun, however, is much further away. If this light source suddenly went out we wouldn't know for eight minutes! That's how long it takes for sunlight to travel through space to Earth.

Light can pass through some, but not all, materials. Materials that light cannot pass through are **opaque**. When light strikes an opaque object it is either reflected (bounced off) or absorbed. Opaque objects cast a shadow.

Light travels in straight lines through **transparent** materials such as glass, air and water. We can see objects clearly through this type of material.

Light can also pass through **translucent** objects. Translucent objects, like the patterned glass we put in bathroom windows, break up the light beams. They do not all pass through in straight lines. It is difficult to see a clear image of the object on the other side of the material.

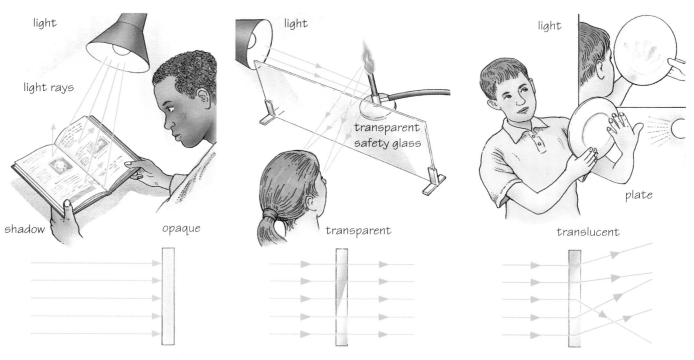

The book is opaque. Light rays cannot pass through it. There is a shadow on the table where light has not been able to reach

A transparent safety screen lets you see the experiment clearly because the light rays pass straight through it

To test if a piece of china is made of fine porcelain, find out if it is translucent. Hold it up to the light. Look for blurry images

Shaped pieces of transparent glass or plastic can do wonderful things to beams of light. When light travelling through air strikes the curved surface of a lens it changes direction. The same thing happens when a beam of light strikes the side of a prism. This is called **refraction**. It happens because light travels more slowly in glass or plastic than it does in air. We use this property of light in the lenses of spectacles and microscopes. Refraction also causes some strange optical illusions.

The pencil seems to be broken

Light reflected from the lower part of the pencil is refracted at the water surface. The brain expects light to travel in straight lines, so light reflected from the lower part of the pencil seems to come from nearer the surface

Collect

- Ray box
- Power supply
- Light beam path sheet
- Mirrors
- Card
- Translucent glass

A ray box is a piece of equipment that produces a bright, sharp beam of light. Use a ray box to carry out three investigations in your group.

Light beams
Investigate what happens to a beam of light when it strikes different materials. Find out if the angle at which the beam strikes the material has any effect.

Record your results on the light beam path sheet. Add any extra experiments you designed and carried out.

Lenses

Look at the available lenses. Think about the ways in which the lenses are different. Suggest two questions that you would like to investigate.

Carry out your investigations using a ray box producing three beams of light. Make drawings to show the effect of the lenses on the light beams.

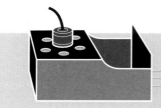 

Use the results of your investigations to complete the poor eyesight sheets.

Prisms

Investigate refraction when light is sent through a prism. Use a single beam of light. Send light through the prism in the three ways shown below. Try other ways too. Make drawings to record your results.

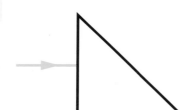 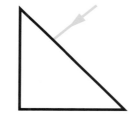 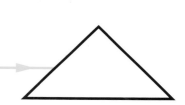

 Write the title *Light* in your book. Make notes including these key points

- Luminous objects
  (What are they? What are some characteristics of light? Include a report on the investigation *Light beams* here.)
- Non-luminous objects
  (How do we see them? What three types are there?)
- Refraction.
  (What is it? Why does it happen? Include reports on the investigations *Lenses* and *Prisms* here.)

B Changing direction

Here are three more investigations. Your teacher will tell you which investigations to carry out.

Collect

- Cartoon sheet
- Lamp
- Mirror

Mirror message

Marlon wants to use a mirror to send a secret message to Yvonne but doesn't want the old man to see. Collect a copy of the cartoon. Draw in the light beams to show how this can happen. Stick it into your book. If you have time, try it out for yourself.

Collect

- Lamp
- Lens
- Card in holder

In the spotlight

CARE

1. Shine a bright light onto a friend's face.
2. Use the lens to project an image of the face onto a small piece of card.
3. Investigate the effect of moving the position of the lens on

- brightness
- clarity
- shape

- 'way up'
- 'way round'
- size

of the image.

Collect

- 250 cm³ beaker

Disappearing penny

Investigate the effect of refraction on the image of a penny at the bottom of a beaker of water. Look at it from all angles. Make drawings to show what you see from each angle (show the penny and the position of your eyes).

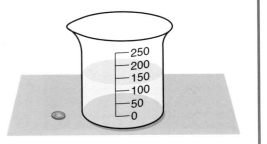

Make your own short notes under the title of each task you completed. Remember to **explain** what happens using your knowledge of the properties of light.

2.3 Colour

A natural spectrum

A White light

Light from the Sun is called **white light**. However, white light is made up of a mixture of colours. When white light is shone at an angle through a prism, the light is split up into these colours, forming a **spectrum**. Raindrops in the air can act like prisms, separating sunlight into a spectrum that we call a rainbow.

All the colours of white light travel at the same speed through space. Space is a vacuum because there are no particles. All the colours travel at the same speed through air too. When light enters a prism, which is denser than air, it slows down and changes direction. This is called refraction. However, in glass or perspex each colour travels at a different speed. Red light travels faster than violet light, so red light doesn't change direction as much as violet light. These differences result in the colours being separated out as a spectrum.

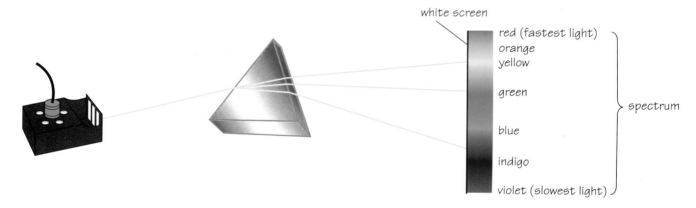

Since you can separate white light from the Sun into its component colours you would expect to be able to make white light by mixing the colours. This is exactly what happens. In fact, you can make white light using just three colours from the spectrum. These are the **primary colours** – blue, green and red. Where these three colours mix white light is produced. Where two of these colours mix **secondary colours** are formed. Your teacher may demonstrate this. All colours of light are formed by mixing the primary colours together in different combinations and with different degrees of brightness.

We see objects because they reflect light from a light source into our eyes. The colour we see depends on the **quality of the reflected light**. Chemical dyes in an object absorb some colours of light and reflect others. The reflected light produces the colour we see. This is true for opaque, translucent and transparent objects. For example, an object that is blue reflects blue light and absorbs all the other colours in white light. A red object reflects red light. A white object reflects all colours. A black object absorbs most light and reflects very little.

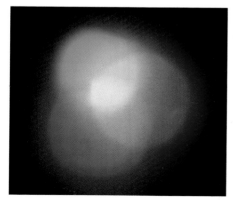

The three primary colours combine to make white light. Where two primary colours overlap secondary colours are formed – cyan, yellow and magenta

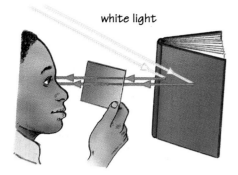

white light

Viewing objects through coloured filters allows us to investigate light in more detail. A red filter reflects red light and also **transmits** (lets through) red light. A yellow filter reflects and transmits red and green light because yellow is a secondary colour made when red and green light combine. When you look at an object through a coloured filter it may appear to be a different colour than it is in bright white light.

Collect

- Red filter
- Blue filter
- Yellow filter
- Coloured objects

You can predict what colour an object will be by following these rules

- remember that the object is lit by white light
- the object reflects the colours that we see and absorbs the others. Work out the reflected colours first
- the filter transmits the colour of the filter and absorbs the rest of the spectrum. Work out the colour or colours transmitted.

Predict the colours you will see when you look at each of the images below through a

- red filter
- blue filter
- yellow filter.

Decide what colours you expect to see

NUS3 NUS3

through the red filter. Write down your predictions and then write down the results. Repeat this for each filter.

Write the title *Light and colour* in your book. Make notes including these key points

- White light
  (Describe what white light is. List the primary and secondary colours.)
- Coloured objects
  (Explain why objects appear the colour they do in white light.)
- Coloured filters.
  (Explain how coloured filters alter the appearance of objects. Include a labelled diagram to show and explain the results of your investigations.)

Collect

- A mystery message sheet

B Mystery message

Use your understanding of coloured light to make a message that can only be seen when viewed through a particular coloured filter.

2.4 Sound investigations

A Sound ideas

When a bell rings we hear it across the other side of the playground almost immediately. This is because **vibrations** from the bell are carried through the air by sound waves at about 330 m/s – very fast but still much slower than the speed of light. As the bell vibrates its surface moves in and out. When it moves out it pushes layers of air closer together. This forms a **compression**, which moves through the air until it reaches our ears. The vibrating bell sends out compression after compression, bombarding the eardrum and making it vibrate in step with the bell. These compressions are what we call a **sound wave**.

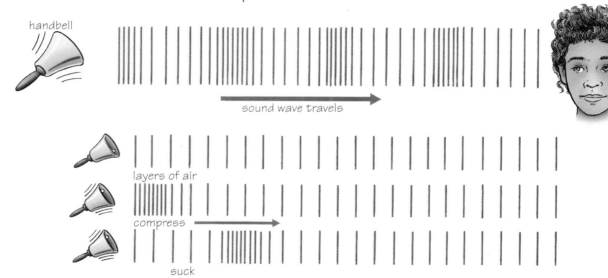

handbell

sound wave travels

layers of air

compress

suck

Sound waves are invisible compressions in air. However, a microphone can pick up the compressions and turn them into an electrical signal. Although this signal cannot be seen, an oscilloscope can freeze and display it as a wave on a television-type screen. An oscilloscope allows us to study two features of a sound wave, the **frequency** and the **amplitude** of the wave.

Frequency refers to the number of vibrations or compressions per second. This affects the **pitch** (how high or low) of the sound.

Amplitude refers to the height of the wave produced by the sound on the oscilloscope. This is a measure of how loud or soft the sound is.

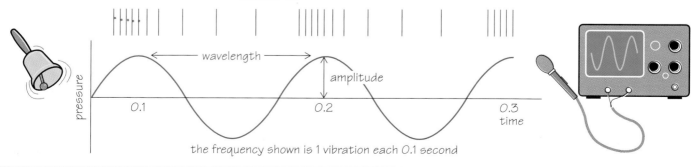

wavelength

amplitude

pressure

0.1   0.2   0.3
time

the frequency shown is 1 vibration each 0.1 second

Work in a group to carry out these investigations. Your teacher may decide to demonstrate part of each.

Collect
- Microphone
- Oscilloscope
- Tuning forks
- Scrap paper

High – low – loud – quiet
Use a tuning fork or whistle into a microphone to produce a simple sound wave on the oscilloscope. Investigate the effect on the wave pattern of

- loud and soft sounds
- high and low sounds.

Make drawings of the results on scrap paper and label them.

Collect
- Help sheet
- Bell
- Stethoscope
- Wooden dowel
- Filter funnel

Sound on the move
You know that sound can travel through air. You have to investigate if sound can travel through a vacuum, through water and through solids. Your teacher will demonstrate the vacuum experiment.

Design your own experiments to find out if sound can travel through liquids and solids. A help sheet is available if you need it.

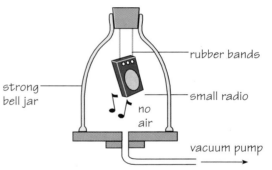

strong bell jar — rubber bands — small radio — no air — vacuum pump

Write the title *Sound ideas* in your book. Make notes including these key points

- How sounds are made
- How sound travels through air
- Pitch and loudness
  (Include the results of your first investigation here.)
- Sound on the move.
  (Include the results of your second investigation here.)

B Sound notes

Collect
- Test tubes and rack
- Ruler
- Plastic beaker
- Elastic band

Make *one* of the simple musical instruments shown below. Investigate how to make a higher or lower note with the instrument. Make labelled drawings to **explain** how it makes a high note and a low note.

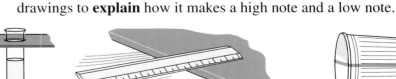

2.5 *Hear here*

A The human ear

Unborn babies love the sound of their parents' voices. A baby will move in the womb to get closer to a gentle voice. As they grow up, children depend on good hearing to develop their speech.

Each part of the ear has a particular job to do. Damage to any part can cause some loss of hearing.

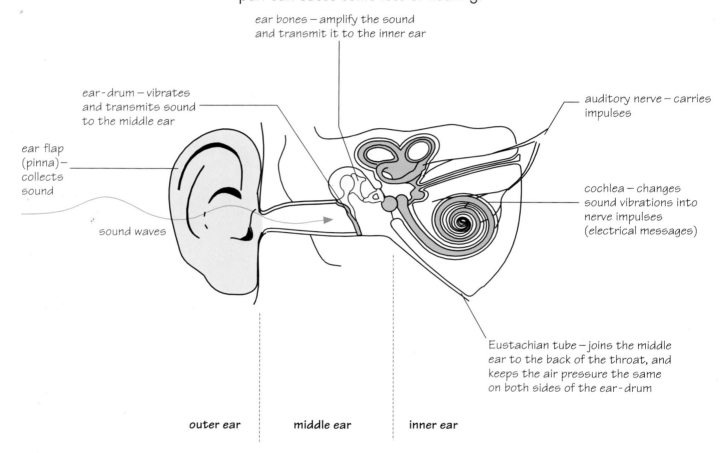

ear bones – amplify the sound and transmit it to the inner ear

ear-drum – vibrates and transmits sound to the middle ear

ear flap (pinna) – collects sound

sound waves

auditory nerve – carries impulses

cochlea – changes sound vibrations into nerve impulses (electrical messages)

Eustachian tube – joins the middle ear to the back of the throat, and keeps the air pressure the same on both sides of the ear-drum

outer ear | middle ear | inner ear

Sound waves enter the ear and strike the ear-drum, which then begins to vibrate. The vibrations are transmitted across the middle ear by three tiny bones – the **hammer**, **anvil** and **stirrup**. These bones also amplify the vibrations. The stirrup passes the vibrations into the **cochlea**, which is coiled like the shell of a snail. In the cochlea the vibrations are changed to electrical signals that are sent to the brain along the **auditory nerve**.

1 Collect and label an ear diagram sheet.
2 Hearing loss can happen when

- the transmission of sound through the ear is upset
- the air pressure on each side of the ear-drum is upset
- the cochlea or auditory nerve is damaged.

Collect and complete the hearing defects sheet.

3 Collect a set of experiment cards. Complete the experiments with a partner. Answer the questions on each card in your book.

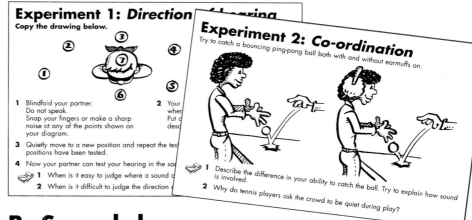

Experiment 1: Direction of hearing
Copy the drawing below.

1 Blindfold your partner.
Do not speak.
Snap your fingers or make a sharp noise at any of the points shown on your diagram.

3 Quietly move to a new position and repeat the test positions have been tested.

4 Now your partner can test your hearing in the sa

  1 When is it easy to judge where a sound c

  2 When is it difficult to judge the direction

2 Your
wher
Put
desc

Experiment 2: Co-ordination
Try to catch a bouncing ping-pong ball both with and without earmuffs on.

1 Describe the difference in your ability to catch the ball. Try to explain how sound is involved.

2 Why do tennis players ask the crowd to be quiet during play?

B Sound damage

Very loud sounds can damage your hearing. In some cases, a loud noise, like an explosion, can tear or make a hole in your ear-drum.

Collect

- Tin can
- Elastic band
- Sheets of plastic
- Pin

Design and carry out an investigation to find the effect a hole or tear has on the quality of sound transmitted. Use a model of the ear-drum in your investigation.

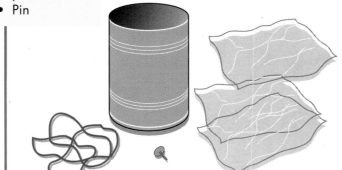

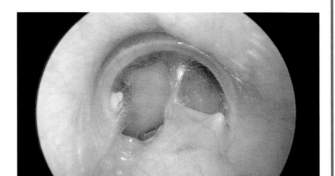

A small perforation of the ear-drum (bottom left)

Decide how to measure the quality of sound.
Decide how and where to damage the 'ear-drum'.

4 Write a short report.
5 Describe your design and the measurements you made.
6 Write a conclusion.

2.6 Problem

Noise annoys

Noise can be a nuisance. Other people's noise can make life miserable. Noisy machines are tiring to work with and can damage our ears.

Your task is to design a box that blocks out the noise from a source such as a small radio or a bleeping watch. The box could represent a room in which you want to play loud music.

Collect

- Materials that you think will absorb sound
- A cardboard box

Design and build your insulated box. Leave enough space for the radio, and don't forget to make a lid!

Work out a way of testing how well the insulation cuts down the noise.

Give your design a mark out of 10 (no difference = 0, perfect insulation = 10).

Then try to improve your design and test it again.

 Write a report (with pictures) that describes

- your design
- how well it did the job
- how you measured the noise reduction
- suggestions for improving your design.

2.7 *Talkabout*

Lacking sight or hearing

Although light and sound waves fill the air, not everyone can receive the messages they carry. The photographs below show signs and aids that are designed to help the blind and deaf.

I'm sorry. Forgive me.

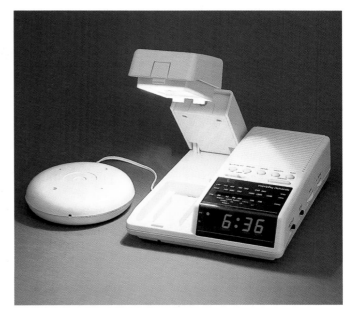

Discuss with a partner where you would find each aid and how it is used.

Make a list of *either* **a** the problems blind people *or* **b** the problems deaf people might meet in your school, and discuss how you could help to solve them.

The world's first photograph, taken by Niépce in 1826, of a courtyard at Gras, France

Print from the world's first negative, taken by Henry Fox Talbot at Lacock Abbey in 1835

The earliest surviving silver-on-glass 'Daguerrotype', 1837, invented by Louis Daguerre

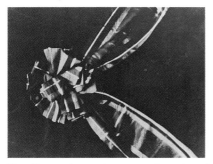

The first colour photograph, taken by Thomas Sutton for James Clerk Maxwell in 1861

The beginnings of photography

In an old science-fiction story written in the 1700s, Tiphaigne de la Roche tells of a long-cherished dream that people had in those days. They wanted to be able to 'fix' the image reflected by a mirror into an instant picture. He wrote

'The elemental spirits . . . have composed a subtle matter, very viscous and quick to harden and dry, by means of which a picture is formed in the twinkling of an eye. They coat a piece of canvas with this matter, and hold it in front of the objects they wish to paint. The first effect of this canvas is similar to that of a mirror; one sees there all objects, near and far, the image of which light can transmit. But what a glass cannot do, the canvas by means of its viscous matter, retains the images . . . This impression of the image is instantaneous, and the canvas is immediately carried away into some dark place. An hour later the impression is dry . . . and you have a picture . . .'

The dream of instant pictures was brought one step closer in 1725 by Professor Johann Schultze. He was trying to make phosphorus by mixing chalk and nitric acid. The acid happened to contain some silver. He performed the experiment near an open window in the sunshine and was surprised to see that the side of the flask facing the window turned purple while the portion away from the light remained white. Tests by the fire proved that the colour change was not due to heat. When he used a mixture containing more silver, the colour appeared more quickly. Then Schultze covered the flask with paper from which he had cut out letters.

'Before long I found that the sun's rays on the side on which they had touched the glass through the apertures in the paper, wrote the words . . . so accurately and distinctly on the chalk sediment, that many people . . . were led to attribute the result to all kinds of artifices.'

Schultze had discovered that silver nitrate, made from the silver and nitric acid, was sensitive to light and could capture images.

Other scientists carried on the search for the 'subtle viscous matter that can form a picture in the twinkling of an eye', but it wasn't until 1826 that the world's first photograph was taken. This needed an exposure of eight hours. Nowadays, photographic film and paper are so sensitive that they can capture the 'mirror image' in a split second. However, they are so easy to use that we can forget how much patient scientific work was needed to invent them.

1 Draw a picture of the experiment Schultze did in the Sun.
2 Describe three things that Schultze did during his experiment that all good scientists should do.
3 Use reference books to find out about and make notes on the following photographic terms
   • ASA
   • developer
   • contact print
   • exposure time
   • f stop
   • fixer.

3
Back to Earth

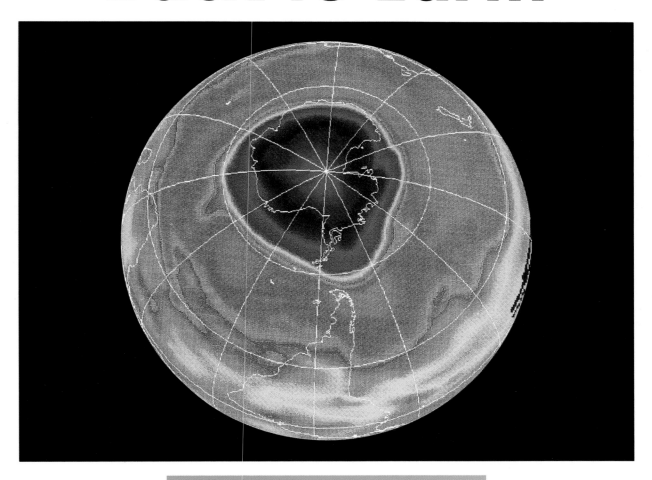

BIG IDEAS IN THIS UNIT

1 The Earth is a ball of rock that orbits a star we call the Sun.
2 Day-light length and seasons are the result of the Earth's position in the solar system.
3 Rocks are mixtures of chemical compounds called minerals. The three types of rock – igneous, sedimentary and metamorphic – were formed by different processes.
4 Rocks can be useful raw materials
 a some metals are extracted from their mineral ores
 b heat energy is released by burning fossil fuels.

3.1 *The Earth and beyond*

A Your address

You live at home. Your home will have a postal address, which will have a number, the name of a street or road and the name of a village or town, district, postcode and country. For example, *10 Downing Street, London, SW1A 2AA, UK*. However, your address could also include . . .

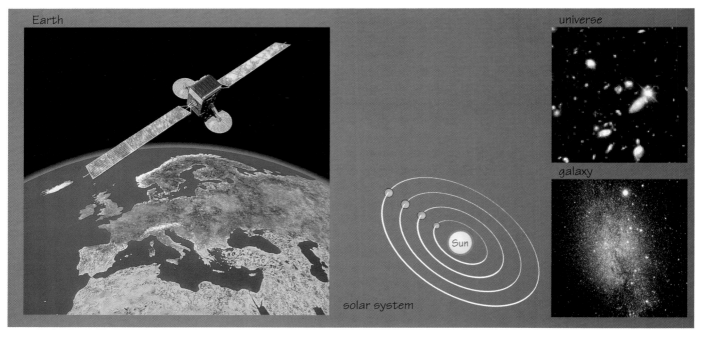

Earth

universe

galaxy

Sun

solar system

The universe

We all live on the Earth, a small blue-green planet that goes around a medium-sized star that we call the Sun. Like all stars, the Sun produces huge amounts of light and heat energy. This means we can see and feel it even though it is 148 800 000 kilometres away. We can also see stars that are even farther away than the Sun.

Our Sun belongs to a group of stars, 100 million of them, that make up the galaxy called the Milky Way. These stars are different sizes and different colours. Our galaxy is just one of about 10 000 million galaxies in the universe. Some galaxies are so far away that the light from all their stars looks as if it is coming from one spot.

The universe is huge. If you could cycle to the Sun, it would take you about 718 years! If you weren't too tired you could keep on pedalling and try to reach the next star in the Milky Way, which is Proxima Centauri. This would take you about 190 million years, not including stops for meals or to find a toilet.

The vast distances in the universe are measured in light years. One light year is the distance that light travels in one year. Our Sun is 8.3 light minutes from Earth whereas Proxima Centauri is 4.22 light years. The Milky Way is 100 000 light years across. The fastest spacecraft can manage only a feeble 0.0001 of the speed of light.

The solar system

The planets in the solar system move around the Sun in a particular path – called an orbit – because of gravitational forces. Planets near to the Sun complete one revolution in a short time; those further away take much longer. Unlike a star, the planets do not make light energy. However, we can see the Moon and planets at night because the Sun's light is reflected by their surfaces.

Artificial satellites have been used to explore the solar system. The chart and diagrams below summarise some of the information that has been discovered.

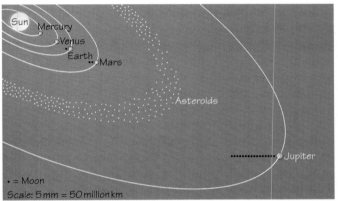

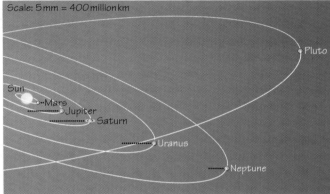

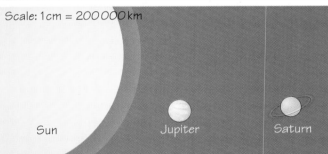

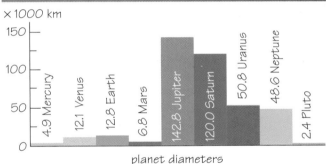

Voyager 2 spacecraft during its closest approach to Saturn and its rings

Part of Jupiter, with two of its Moons in the foreground

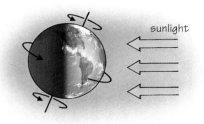

sunlight

The Earth

The Earth is a ball of rock with liquid in the middle. It has a very thin layer of water and soil on the surface. The Earth spins or rotates from west to east as it orbits the Sun.

Why do we have day and night?
There is one complete rotation of the Earth every 24 hours. So your home moves slowly from sunlight into darkness every day. When you are in the sunlight, the opposite side of the Earth is in darkness.

Why do we have the seasons?
If your home is in the northern hemisphere, it is tilted towards the Sun during the summer. This means that the Sun is high in the sky and the surface is warmed. At the same time the southern hemisphere is tilted away from the Sun, which is low in the sky thus making the surface colder. This is winter. Half a year later the Earth has moved to the other side of the Sun. The north is tilted away and has winter; the south is tilted towards and has summer.

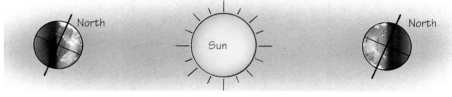

Summer in the northern hemisphere   Winter in the northern hemisphere

Write the title *The Earth in space* in your book. Make notes including these key points

- Your address in the universe
- Orbits
- Day and night
  (Include a diagram.)

- The solar system
  (Include a drawing.)
- Light from stars and planets
- The seasons. (Include diagrams.)

Collect

- Solar system sheet
- Earth orbit sheet
- Scissors
- 2 paper fasteners
- Coloured pencils

Solar system
1 Make the solar system disc (follow the instructions on the sheet).
2 Use the information in this topic to complete the disc. Stick it into your book.

Earth orbit
1 Make the model of Earth's orbit (follow the instructions on the sheet).
2 Discuss with a partner how the model can be used to demonstrate

- why we have night and day
- the reason for having different seasons
- why temperature and day-light length should be different in summer and winter.

3 Complete the information on the model. Stick it into your book.

B Stars and planets

Collect

- Lamp
- Ball
- Coin

Work in pairs for this activity.

Use the lamp to represent the Sun and the ball to represent the Earth. Toss a coin to decide which demonstration each person has to do.

HEADS
Use the model to explain night and day to your partner

TAILS
Use the model to explain the seasons to your partner

1 Collect an evaluation sheet. In the description box write what you did. In the comment box your partner should write a comment about the quality of your explanation.

2 Certain telescopes can take photographs from outside the Earth's atmosphere. Examine the photographs below. Identify which one shows

- a star
- a galaxy
- a planet
- a moon.

Explain your choices.

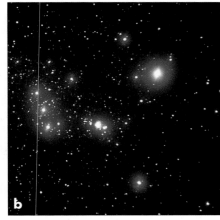

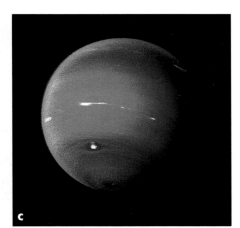

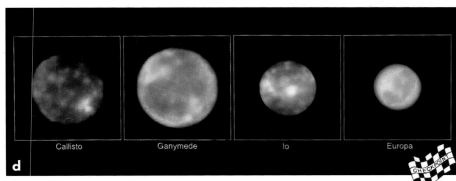

Callisto   Ganymede   Io   Europa

3.2 *Inside the Earth*

A Through the Earth

The Earth is about 4.6 billion years old. For most of that time there was no life on Earth. People have only been on the planet for the last 0.003 billion years. That's like turning up at 12 seconds to midnight for a party that started at 7 p.m. and finishes at midnight!

The Earth formed when lots of particles were attracted together because of gravity. The lump of material got bigger and bigger and eventually formed a planet.

The Earth is 12 700 kilometres in diameter. Imagine that you could travel right through it. What would you see and hear and feel?

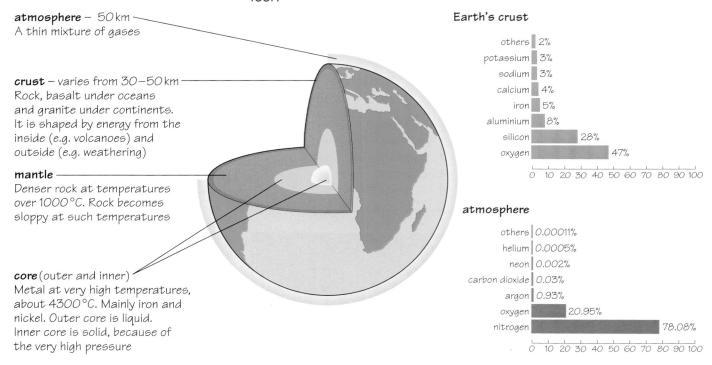

atmosphere – 50 km
A thin mixture of gases

crust – varies from 30–50 km
Rock, basalt under oceans
and granite under continents.
It is shaped by energy from the
inside (e.g. volcanoes) and
outside (e.g. weathering)

mantle
Denser rock at temperatures
over 1000 °C. Rock becomes
sloppy at such temperatures

core (outer and inner)
Metal at very high temperatures,
about 4300 °C. Mainly iron and
nickel. Outer core is liquid.
Inner core is solid, because of
the very high pressure

Earth's crust

others	2%
potassium	3%
sodium	3%
calcium	4%
iron	5%
aluminium	8%
silicon	28%
oxygen	47%

0 10 20 30 40 50 60 70 80 90 100

atmosphere

others	0.00011%
helium	0.0005%
neon	0.002%
carbon dioxide	0.03%
argon	0.93%
oxygen	20.95%
nitrogen	78.08%

0 10 20 30 40 50 60 70 80 90 100

Write the title *Through the Earth* in your book. Make notes including these key points

- An imaginary journey **through** the Earth, from the top of the atmosphere (the stratosphere) above the UK to the stratosphere above Australia
(Describe your journey as fully as you can. Use reference material plus the diagrams above to help you find the necessary facts. You can also use your imagination to introduce an element of science fiction.)
- A labelled map of the Earth.
(Use a pencil and compass (or the circular bottom of a container) to draw a circle. The pencil line represents the thin layer of atmosphere and crust. Label this. Complete the 'map' by adding the other layers that you would have travelled through on your imaginary journey.)

B Crust detective

The Earth's crust is made of rock – a hard solid substance. However, its shape can be changed by pushing- and pulling-type forces. Sometimes the energy for these changes is available very quickly, as in a landslide or a volcanic eruption. At other times the energy transforms the land very slowly, as in the erosion of a river valley.

1 How can these geological formations be explained?
2 What do they suggest about the history of the area?
3 What do you think they will look like in a million years from now?

a These Austrian mountains are far from the sea, yet their rocks contain fossils of tiny sea creatures

b A lava tube in Hawaii

c A sea stack in the Orkney Islands

d Folded rock layers near Lulworth in Dorset

e Part of the Grand Canyon in Arizona

3.3 Rock groups

A Types of rock

The rocks that you can pick up on a beach, on a mountain or in the garden were made many many years ago. They are all mixtures of chemical compounds called **minerals**. There are three main types of rock: **igneous**, **sedimentary** and **metamorphic**. The rock cycle below shows how new rock is formed over long periods of time by processes on the Earth's surface and by processes deep within the Earth. The different types of rocks have different textures and also contain different minerals.

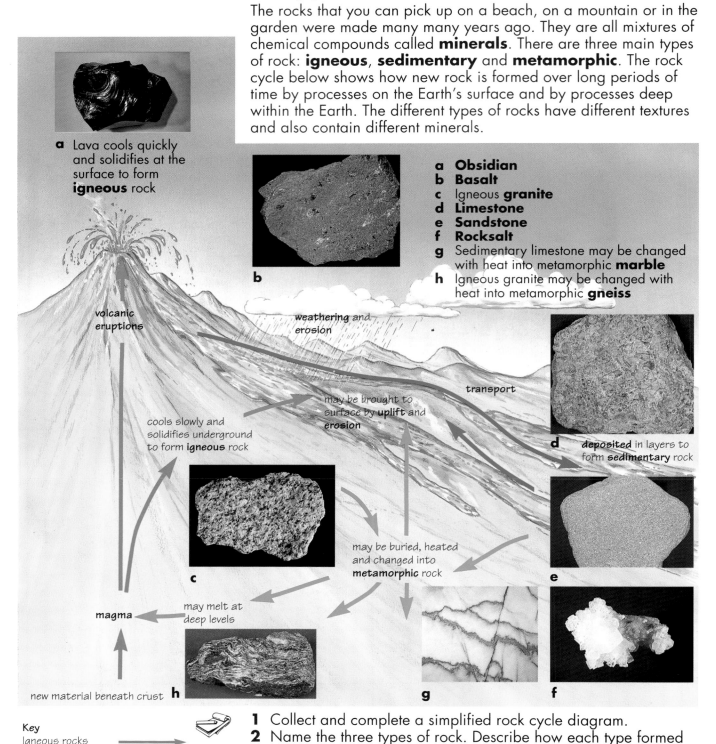

a Lava cools quickly and solidifies at the surface to form **igneous** rock

a **Obsidian**
b **Basalt**
c Igneous **granite**
d **Limestone**
e **Sandstone**
f **Rocksalt**
g Sedimentary limestone may be changed with heat into metamorphic **marble**
h Igneous granite may be changed with heat into metamorphic **gneiss**

volcanic eruptions

weathering and erosion

transport

cools slowly and solidifies underground to form **igneous** rock

may be brought to surface by **uplift** and **erosion**

may be buried, heated and changed into **metamorphic** rock

d **deposited** in layers to form **sedimentary** rock

magma

may melt at deep levels

new material beneath crust

Key
Igneous rocks
Sedimentary rocks
Metamorphic rocks

1 Collect and complete a simplified rock cycle diagram.
2 Name the three types of rock. Describe how each type formed and name two examples of each type.
3 Look up and write down the meanings of 'weathering' and 'erosion'.

Collect

- Large jar
- Soil sample
- Ruler
- Cold and warm microscope slides
- Microscope
- Pipette
- Salol
- Wet clay
- Safety glasses

CARE

Do not inhale the fumes!

The following activities use models to show how each rock type forms.

Sedimentary rocks

1 Add water to the jar until it is two-thirds full. Measure the depth of water.
2 Pour the soil sample into the jar and swirl it gently. Allow the soil to settle.
3 Measure the new depth of water and the depth of the sediment.
4 Repeat the measurements next lesson.

Igneous rocks

When molten salol cools it crystallises. Investigate the effect of speed of cooling on the appearance of the salol crystals.

Metamorphic rocks

Use wet clay to make two identical models. Leave one model to dry on the windowsill. Ask your teacher to bake the other in an oven or a kiln. Investigate the strength and texture of each model.

4 What are rocks made from?
5 Write a short report on each experiment. Remember to write a conclusion.

B Rocky relations

Collect

- Samples of sedimentary, igneous and metamorphic rock

Examine the samples of rock. Also examine the photographs opposite. Compare the samples with the photographs and identify the rock sample that

- formed from cooling lava
- formed underground under great pressure and heat
- was deposited in water.

 Write about your findings.

3.4 Rock properties

A Rock roadshow

A **resource** is a raw material that can be made into something useful. Rocks are very important resources, because of their physical properties. For example, the top layer of a road is made up of pieces of rock bonded together by **bitumen**. Not every rock, however, is suitable for road making. The road surface should

- be hard
- weather slowly
- prevent water from passing through it
- prevent cars from skidding.

To match these requirements the rock selected must have certain physical properties.

a Most of the minerals in the rock should have a hardness greater than 5 on the **hardness scale** (see below).

b The rock fragments must wear unevenly to make a skid-free surface. At least two different minerals of different hardness should be present.

c The rock fragments should have a rough surface for the bitumen to stick to.

d The rock must not let water through, nor shatter in cold weather. (In other words, it must stand up to weathering.)

e The rock should not be damaged by acid.

Collect

- 3 rock samples
- Information card
- Hand lens
- Nail
- Glass slide
- Steel blade
- Metal file
- Bottle of acid
- Dropper
- Safety glasses

Investigate the properties of the three rock samples to identify the best roadstone. Record your results in a checklist.

Compare the rocks by

- using available information
- making observations
- designing and carrying out tests for properties (d) and (e) above
- estimating their hardness using the tests below.

Hardness scale

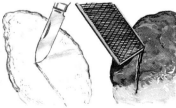

| fingernail crushes | fingernail scratches | iron nail scratches | glass scratches | steel blade scratches | metal file scratches |

Write a report of your investigation for the civil engineer in charge of building the road.

Describe the tests you did.

Recommend one of the rocks for the road's surface.

B Physical properties

The rocks and minerals shown are raw materials. These rocks are important to us because of their properties.

Slate ... for roof tiles

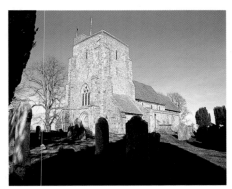

Sandstone ... for building

Coal ... for fuel

Chalk ... for teachers!

 For each example above write down

- why they are useful raw materials
- the properties that make them useful raw materials.

3.5 *Rock burns*

A Fossil fuels

Some rocks are useful raw materials because of their physical properties, like strength or hardness. Other rocks contain useful substances. For example, the minerals called **ores** are metal-containing compounds and the metal can be freed by using energy (see page 76). Examples of ores include malachite (a compound of copper) and haematite (a compound of iron).

Then there are fuel-bearing rocks, which contain compounds that burn well to release a lot of heat energy. The fossil fuels coal, oil and natural gas are particularly important.

Where did fossil fuels come from?
Fossil fuels formed millions of years ago from the remains of living things.

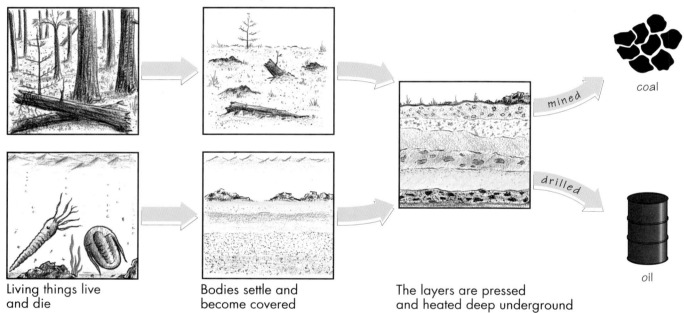

Living things live and die

Bodies settle and become covered

The layers are pressed and heated deep underground

coal

oil

What are fossil fuels?
Coal is a black solid that is mined from the ground. It is a mixture of different substances, most of which burn well.

Oil is a black liquid that is released from the ground by drilling a hole. It is a mixture of different substances, most of which burn well.

Natural gas is an invisible gas that is released from the ground by drilling a hole. It is mainly methane and it burns very well.

Fossil fuels can cause air pollution when they burn. For example, sulphur dioxide, an acidic gas, is formed when coal and oil burn. Other acidic gases, nitrogen oxides, are formed by the combustion of fuel in car engines. These gases dissolve in water droplets in clouds, forming acid rain. Carbon dioxide is also formed when fossil fuels burn. Increased levels of this gas in the atmosphere are causing an increase in the greenhouse effect, which might lead to global warming.

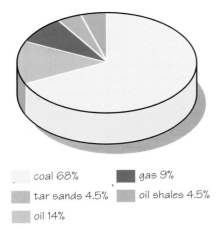

coal 68%   gas 9%

tar sands 4.5%   oil shales 4.5%

oil 14%

Remaining world reserves

How long will fossil fuels last?

These fuels cannot last forever. They are also irreplaceable. The pie chart shows how much of each type of fuel is left. The world's oil reserves may only last another 40 years or so.

Write the title *Fossil fuels* in your book. Make notes including these key points

- The formation of oil
  (Include a labelled diagram.)
- The world's oil and coal supplies are limited
- Fossil fuel pollution.
  (A diagram is available to help you; ask your teacher.)

Collect

- Separating apparatus
- Small bits of coal
- Beaker of water
- Bunsen burner and heatproof mat
- Wooden splint
- pH paper
- Safety glasses
- Clamp stand

1 Set up the apparatus as shown. Ensure that there is ventilation in the room.

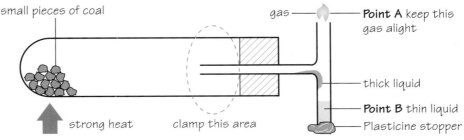

small pieces of coal   gas   **Point A** keep this gas alight

thick liquid

Point B thin liquid

strong heat   clamp this area   Plasticine stopper

2 Heat the coal strongly. **Keep trying** to burn the gas that is released (at point A).
3 When the gas flame drops stop heating and allow to cool. Examine the liquid at point B. Test it with pH paper.
4 Open the tube. Drop the remains of the coal into water in a beaker.

1 Draw a labelled diagram of your experiment.
2 The word equation for this reaction is

   coal → coal gas + clear liquid + tar + solid remains

   What properties of each of the products did you discover?
3 What evidence is there that coal is a mixture of different substances?

B Spot the pollutant

What is the link between fossil fuels and the effects shown in the photos? What could be done to reduce each one?

3.6 Problem

Is there anybody out there?

Spacecraft that were launched in the 1970s and 1980s to study the planets have now left our solar system and are continuing to travel into outer space. They will take many thousands of years to reach the nearest stars. Each spacecraft carries a message from Earth to any intelligent life forms that might locate it. The plaque below is attached to the side of *Pioneer 10* launched in 1972. It was the first spaceship to leave our solar system, in 1989.

The *Pioneer 10* plaque was carefully designed to show what kind of beings launched the spacecraft, from where and when. The diagram on the left shows the Sun's position relative to 14 pulsars (stars emitting radio energy) and enables the time elapsed since the launch to be calculated

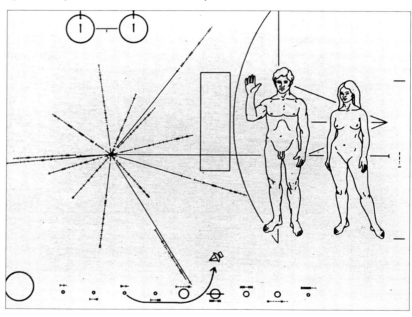

Collect

- Poster paper
- Coloured pencils
- Tape recorder
- Blank tape

Work in a small team.

Design and produce your own interstellar message to send into space. There must be three parts to your team's message

- a plaque for the outside of the spacecraft
- a short tape of Earth sounds
- a set of five Earth objects.

1 Discuss why the images on the *Pioneer* plaque were chosen.
2 Design your own plaque on poster paper. Make a key for the images you have chosen to show.
3 Discuss what sounds should go on your audio tape. Record these.
4 Discuss what objects you would send. Collect these if you can.
5 Select the best ideas from the class. Assemble the whole 'interstellar message'.

1 Write a complete description of the interstellar message and explain why you have chosen each image, sound and object. Include a drawing of the plaque.
2 Bury the message in the school grounds – you never know what kind of living thing will dig it up in the future.

3.7 *Talkabout*

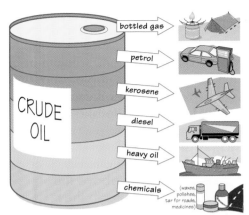

Disappearing fossil fuels

Natural fossil fuels cannot last forever.
What do you think we'll have to do when the oil supplies run out?
How will your life change?
What can be done NOW to make the oil last longer?

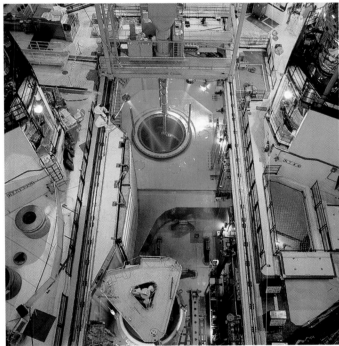

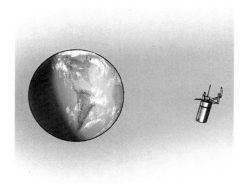

Most communications satellites are in geostationary orbits

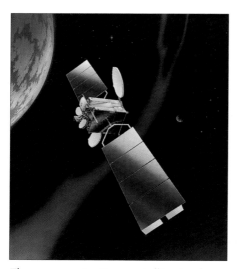

The communications satellite *Intelsat VIII*

Geostationary satellites

If you telephone a friend on another continent your message can go either via a cable under the sea or via a communications satellite in space. The journey by satellite is much longer than by cable, and the message has to be coded and sent by radio waves. Even so, it takes less than half a second to travel out to the satellite and back down to your friend on Earth.

The satellites that relay these messages are 35 800 km above the equator and move round in an orbit that takes exactly one day. The Earth also rotates once in a day, so the satellites stay above the same place on the equator. This means that from the Earth they seem to be stationary in the sky. Dish antennae can then easily be pointed at the satellites to send and receive messages.

The International Telecommunications Satellite Organisation (Intelsat) currently has 25 satellites in orbit serving over 200 countries around the world. *Intelsat VIII* satellites are geostationary satellites and some were launched after 1996. Each satellite can handle 82 000 telephone calls and 500 TV channels at the same time. It is a body-stabilised satellite and looks rather like a box with solar panel 'wings'. Inside the satellite, there are momentum wheels that are used together with thrusters to keep the satellite properly facing the Earth.

Intelsat VIII has a mass of 1595 kg – the mass of an average family car – and has an expected life of about 13 to 16 years. After this time it runs out of power and a small booster rocket sends it out into a higher orbit, where it cannot get in the way of other working satellites. A replacement can then be launched to take over the work of the original.

Intelsat VIII has a number of dish antennae that receive signals from Earth, boost them and then send them back. The power to do this is provided by solar panels and back-up batteries. The batteries are needed during solar eclipses. The total power used by the satellite is 5 kW – less than an electric cooker.

1 Why are dish aerials needed to receive satellite television programmes? In which direction should these dishes be pointed?
2 Geostationary satellites have to be in orbits above the equator. Can you explain why this is so?
3 If a tennis ball represents the Earth, how far away from it would a geostationary satellite have to be on the same scale? (The Earth's radius is about 6400 km.)
4 Use the books in the classroom and books and other resources from a library to find out more about satellites. Key words to look up in the index are: weather (satellite), telecommunications, Telstar, spy satellite.

4
Body and mind

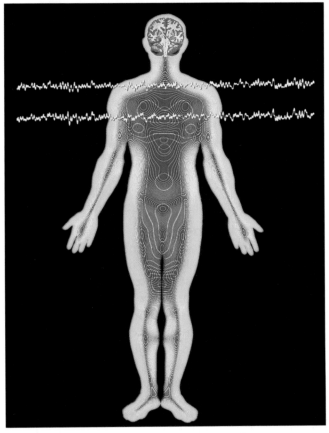

BIG IDEAS IN THIS UNIT

1 There is variation between species and within a species.

2 Variation within a species can be caused by inherited characteristics and by environmental factors.

3 Selective breeding is used to improve the characteristics of a species and to produce new varieties of a species.

4 Physical, emotional and mental changes take place during human development.

5 Human movement depends on the action of the skeleton, joints and muscles.

6 The brain controls movement, co-ordination, thinking and learning, and the emotions.

4.1 *Who are you?*

A Variation

Scientists classify organisms by looking for similarities and differences. The differences between two different species are often very clear. For example, a dolphin is very different from a lion, even though they are both mammals. Within a species there is some **variation** but much less than there is between species.

We all belong to the group called human beings because we have so much in common.

The differences you can see between individual humans are caused by

- **genetics** – information inherited from the **genes** of our parents, which is expressed (shows up) as physical or chemical characteristics
- **environmental factors** – that can affect the way our genes are expressed. Of course the environment can affect you directly too. If you fell and cut your knee you might have a scar there. This has nothing to do with genetics.

Genetic variation

Most body features and some patterns of behaviour are passed from parents to child in the form of genes. Genes are like the pieces of a giant jigsaw puzzle. All together they are a complete and detailed blueprint for making you.

Genes are found in the nucleus of a cell. Each gene is a piece of chemical code. The code contains the instructions for carrying out various tasks at various times during the construction, growth and development of your body. Some characteristics, like the ability to roll your tongue, are controlled by a single gene. In any population, some people can roll their tongues and some cannot. This is an example of **discontinuous variation**. Other characteristics, such as height, are more complex and are controlled by many genes. In any population there is a shortest person and a tallest person with people of lots of different heights in between. Height is a characteristic that shows **continuous variation**.

Discontinuous variation

Continuous variation

Genes are inherited in this way.

Most body cells have two genes for each characteristic

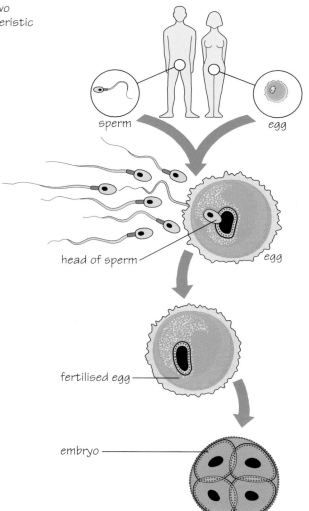

sperm

egg

head of sperm

egg

fertilised egg

embryo

1 Sex cells carry one gene for each characteristic

2 At fertilisation the sperm nucleus and the egg nucleus join

3 There are now two genes for each characteristic in the fertilised egg – one from each parent

4 The cell divides and an embryo grows

Environmental variation

Environmental factors affect the way genes are **expressed** (show themselves). For example, some plants, like heather, grow better in acidic soils; in the wrong soil conditions heathers do not grow strongly. Other examples are shown below.

Apples picked from different parts of the same tree

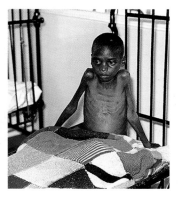

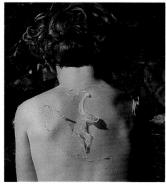

Collect

- Graph paper
- Coloured pencils
- Ruler

Variation survey 1: Continuous variation

Work in a small group.

Your group should carry out a class survey to find the **range** of *either* hand span *or* shoe size (a measure of foot length).

Hand span

Measure the hand span, to the nearest mm, of at least 20 pupils.

Group the measurements into 2 cm ranges (13.1–15 cm, 15.1–17 cm etc.)

Make a tally of the number of measurements in each range. Draw a bar chart of the results.

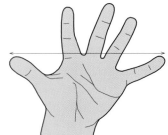

Shoe size

Find the shoe size, to the nearest half size, of at least 20 pupils.

Group the measurements into three half-size ranges ($3–4\frac{1}{2}$, $5–6\frac{1}{2}$ etc.)

Make a tally of the number of measurements in each range. Draw a bar chart of the results.

or

Collect your data and enter it into a spreadsheet. Use the program to produce a bar chart.

Variation survey 2: Discontinuous variation

Carry out a survey of **one** of the characteristics shown below. Talk to at least 20 pupils.

Ability to roll your tongue

tongue roller   non-tongue roller

Presence or absence of ear lobes

free ear lobe   fixed ear lobe

Decide on the best way to record the results of your survey.

Write the title *Variation* in your book. Make notes including these key points

- Genetic factors
  (Explain how we inherit characteristics. A labelled drawing might be useful.
  Use your graph of hand span or shoe size to explain what continuous variation is.
  Use your information on tongue rolling or ear lobes to explain what discontinuous variation is.)
- Environmental factors.
  (Explain the effect of the environment on variation by describing any two of the examples shown on page 51.)

B Spot the variation

before

after

Look at the examples of variation above. Make a table to show which are caused by genes and which are caused by the environment.

4.2 Grow up

A Changes

Growth from baby to adult involves many changes

- physical – to do with size, movement and co-ordination
- mental – to do with the ability to learn, think and reason
- emotional and social – to do with understanding and learning to control our feelings, and dealing with other people.

Some key stages of development are shown below.

	4 months old	4 years old	14 years old
Physical development	Rapid growth Can sit with support Hand and eye movements co-ordinated	Growing quickly and in good control of most muscles Beginning to catch and bounce a ball	Increasing in strength Reaching puberty Good co-ordination and control
Mental development	Rapid development of centre for co-ordination	Enjoys fantasy and pretend situations Uses imagination Language developing rapidly	Learning a lot of new ideas and values Powers of reasoning and problem solving are developing
Emotional and social development	Self-centred and totally dependent on parents and family	Behaviour depends on rewards and punishments Enjoys playing with other people of all ages Learns to share	Listens to other people's views, can understand rules and regulations Enjoys contact with people of own age

Collect

- A size data sheet

a Find the missing numbers

b In what order did they finish the race?
The turtle ran faster than the hare.
The turtle ran slower than the snail.
The hare ran faster than the mouse

Physical development

1 Copy and complete the boxes of the flow chart to show the most important physical changes at each age.

baby → toddler → teenager

2 Using the size data sheet, draw two line graphs to show recommended weight ranges for the heights shown – one for women and one for men.

Mental development

1 What does 'mental development' mean?

2 Very few people younger than you could solve the following problems. Work with a partner to get the answers.

c (i) Move one coin only to make two rows of four coins

c (ii) Move three matches only to make four equal squares

B Child care

The photographs below show examples of conditions and experiences that young children need.

Describe how each situation helps in the development of the child.

4.3 Muscle power

A Skeleton and joints

There is a great deal of variation in human growth. The genes you inherit from your parents determine how tall you have the potential to be. Reaching this height depends on environmental factors. You have control over many of these environmental factors, such as the amount and quality of food you eat, whether or not you take exercise, whether or not you avoid smoking, drug taking and so on.

As you grow the bones of your skeleton get longer and stronger. You produce more muscle tissue and your movement becomes well co-ordinated.

The skeleton has three important jobs to do. It provides a **framework** to support the body. It also gives **protection** to the heart, lungs, kidneys, brain and spinal cord, and the delicate organs of the digestive system. It also provides points to anchor the muscles. Together muscles and bones allow **movement**.

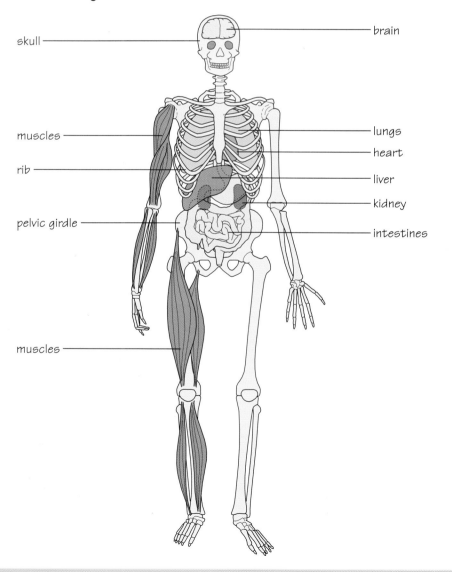

skull — brain

muscles — lungs

rib — heart

— liver

pelvic girdle — kidney

— intestines

muscles

Bones move against each other at **joints**. Your muscles provide the force needed to move your bones. Movement depends on two muscle sets at each joint. Because they work against each other they are called **antagonistic muscles**. When one muscle **contracts** (shortens) to pull on a bone the other muscle **relaxes** (lengthens). Muscles always work in pairs like this because they can only provide a **pulling force**. Muscles never push.

At some joints, such as those in the skull and pelvis, the bones are completely **fused** or joined together. There is no movement here. Some joints allow only partial movement – like the backbone where the individual bones are separated by discs of cartilage.

At other joints in the skeleton movement is much more free. These are called **synovial joints** and there are several different kinds

- **hinge**
- **ball and socket**
- **gliding**
- **pivot**.

Each type of joint allows movement in a particular direction. The structure of a synovial joint is shown below.

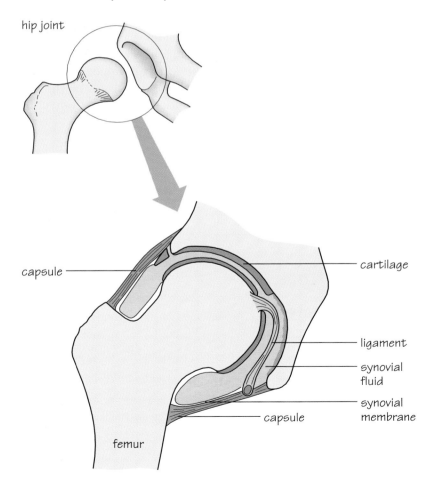

hip joint

capsule

cartilage

ligament

synovial fluid

synovial membrane

capsule

femur

Collect

- Newton balance
- Summary sheet

Carry out the three sets of experiments described below.

Leg muscles

1 Sit on a chair.
2 Place your hand on the muscle at the back of your thigh. Slowly swing your leg back and forth under the chair.
3 Repeat instruction **2** but with your hand on the muscle at the front of your thigh.

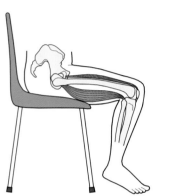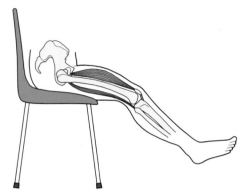

Arm muscles

1 Roll up one sleeve.
2 Show off your upper arm muscles like a body builder.
3 Watch the muscle at the front of your arm – the **biceps**.
4 Straighten your arm. Look at the muscle at the back – the **triceps**.

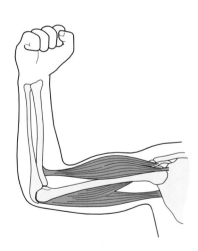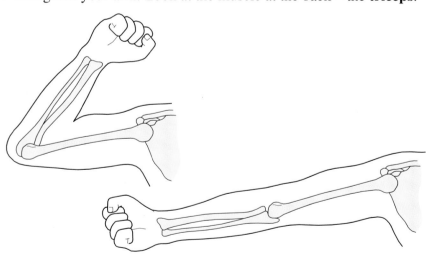

Muscle power

1 Use the Newton balance to measure the force your muscles exert. Follow the instructions on the summary sheet.
2 Collect class results and use a computer spreadsheet program to produce graphs showing the average force applied by each muscle group. Display these in the class.

Write the title *The skeleton and movement* in your book. Make notes including these key points

- Functions of the skeleton
- A typical joint
  (Copy the diagram on page 57. Use books to find the function of each labelled part. Label your diagram to **explain** what each part does.)
- Antagonistic muscle action.
  (Explain what the term means. Copy and complete the arm drawings opposite to show the shape of the biceps and triceps.)

B Types of joint

Collect

- What you need for this activity

Work with a partner or in a small group to share the work in these tasks.

Moving joints
Use available resources or make observations of each other's movements to find the type of movement that takes place at each of the four types of synovial joint listed on page 57.

Record the results of your research in the form of a table. Suitable headings are

- type of joint
- example
- movement at joint.

Flexible joints
Collect measurements on how flexible each member of the group is. Decide on how to measure the flexibility in the following stretching exercises.

How far can you rotate your arms?

How far below your knee can you reach?

How close to your toes can you get?

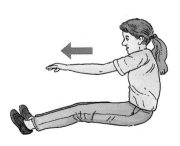

Display your results, including the group average, in a table.

4.4 *Learning*

A Brain work

The human brain is truly amazing. It weighs about 1.3 kg and can think faster than the most expensive computer. It can do far more jobs than any machine. Even more importantly, it can learn new facts and skills. The brain is made up of millions of tiny nerve cells, which can pass messages to each other. They work together to do all sorts of important jobs.

Key
1 Thinking, memory, emotion
2 Hearing
3 Sight
4 Movement
5 Co-ordination
6 Breathing, digestion, heart rate

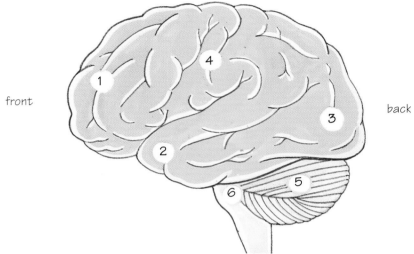

Work with a partner in the next two activities.

Collect

- Star drawing apparatus
- 4 star shapes
- Stop-clock
- Mirror

Memory test
Imagine that you have just witnessed a bank robbery. There is a picture of the robber on the classroom wall. Stand about one metre away from it. Your partner will uncover the picture for 10 seconds only. Write a full description of the robber in the picture.

Learning test
1 Sit on a stool. Adjust the mirror so that you can see the star drawing.
2 Look in the mirror only (no cheating!). Time how long it takes to draw round the star keeping between the lines. Repeat this with the other three star shapes.

1 Write the best description you can of the human brain. Use the information and drawing above.
2 What jobs must your brain be doing now as you answer these questions?

3 Describe the memory test. What was accurate about your description of the robber? What was inaccurate?
4 Write a report of the learning test.
Include a table of results with two columns. Did you improve with practice?

B Ways of learning

As you know, there are lots of facts to learn at school. Your memory can be improved if you sort facts into groups.

Collect

- 2 trays of objects
- Stop-clock

You have 30 seconds to do each of the tasks described below. After each task go back to your seat and write down the names of as many of the objects on the tray as you can.

1 Go to tray 1.
Look at it for 30 seconds only.
2 Go to tray 2.
Arrange the objects into four groups in 30 seconds.

5 Is your first or second list most correct?
Did sorting things into sets help you to remember them?
6 The cartoons show some different ways of learning.

a Doing

b Observing

c Listening

Give an example of something you have learned in each of these ways.

4.5 *Problem*

Teamwork

Your own social development can be helped by working together with people of your own age. Work in a different group from usual to solve **one** of the problems below. You will be in competition with the other teams to find the best solution. The most successful team is likely to be the one where

- everybody is allowed to have his/her say
- decisions are made quickly
- everybody understands the solution or plan
- everyone has a job to do.

Design and build

The problem
Design and build a structure to transport a marble from its starting point to a cup in exactly 15 seconds.

Rules
1 The structure must be able to stand up by itself.
2 Once the marble is released it cannot be touched again, nor can the structure.

Equipment
- 1 sheet of cardboard
- 1 sheet of poster paper
- 1 newspaper
- 1 roll of tape
- 1 box of pins
- 1 metre of string
- 3 plastic cups
- 3 elastic bands
- Some plasticine
- Stop-clock

Hints
- Discuss possible solutions to the problem.
- Decide on the best solution.
- Make sure everyone understands the chosen solution. Make a sketch of the structure you intend to build.
- Divide out the work and build your structure.

Hold a competition to compare structures.

Computer simulation

The problem
Use a computer simulation program to solve a problem. It could be a program like Sim Town (pictured above) or Dogz or it could be a program on designing an experiment.

Rules
In the time available, score the highest possible rating on the simulation.

Equipment
- Computer
- Simulation software
- Scrap paper

Hints
- Learn the rules and controls quickly.
- Make sure everyone understands the aim of the simulation.
- Decide on the best solution or strategy to use.
- Everyone should contribute to the decisions that have to be made as the simulation runs. Make decisions quickly.

Compare your results with those of other teams.

1 Describe the problem you had to solve.
2 Describe your solution.

- Make a drawing if you did 'Design and build' and label it to show how it works.
- Decide on the best way to record your solution if you did 'Computer simulation'.

3 How could you have improved your teamwork?

Genetic engineering

We now understand genetics quite well. We can use this knowledge to benefit humankind in many ways through genetic engineering. However, every new development that involves altering genes or combining them in new and different ways has to be considered very carefully. There are many concerns.

Talk about each example of genetic engineering shown below. For each make a list of benefits and a list of concerns.

Cloned sheep – Megan and Morag

It is now possible to produce sheep that are genetically identical (clones) by replacing the nucleus of a fertilised egg cell. The new cell is implanted in the uterus of a ewe and develops normally there

Genetically engineered tomatoes

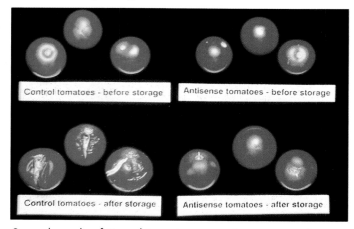

Control tomatoes - before storage

Antisense tomatoes - before storage

Control tomatoes - after storage

Antisense tomatoes - after storage

Some brands of tinned tomatoes contain tomatoes that have been genetically altered using viruses. These tomatoes last longer in the tin

Transgenic pigs

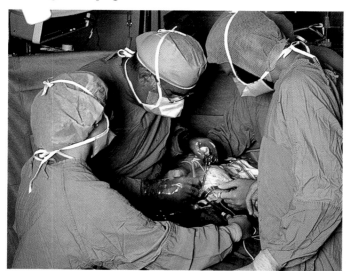

In the future, hearts from transgenic pigs may be used for human transplants. Transgenic pigs carry some human genes to help prevent rejection of the heart by the tissues of the person receiving it

Insulin

People with diabetes need insulin to control their blood sugar level. Human insulin is now produced by bacteria that have been genetically altered to carry the human insulin gene

4.7 *Readabout*

A primitive wheat variety

Selective breeding

Ten thousand years ago our early ancestors began to settle in small communities and some became farmers. They knew nothing about **genetics** – the science of inheritance. However, they grew cereal crops such as wheat and barley and they domesticated animals like sheep and cattle for food. These plants and animals were all carefully selected from the wild. Seeds were taken from wild wheat plants that had both many and large grains. When these plants were grown and harvested, some of the grain was kept back for planting the following year. In the same way, the fattest, least fierce cattle were taken from the wild and allowed to breed in order to produce a herd.

An example of early European cattle

Early farmers made sure that crop plants and animals passed their useful characteristics from one generation to the next. They did this by **artificial selection** of the best plants and animals to be the parents for the next generation. This is called **selective breeding**.

Nowadays we have quite a good understanding of genetics. We can predict the likely outcomes of plant- or animal-breeding programmes. Today artificial selection and selective breeding have two uses

1 to improve the characteristics of a plant or animal variety. For example all crop plants in this country are bred to be resistant to disease and frost, and to have a long supermarket shelf-life by ripening slowly
2 to develop new varieties: producing all the modern varieties of cats and dogs for example.

Modern commercial strains of chicken selected for egg production (left) and for meat yield (right) at seven weeks of age. Their weights differ by more than fourfold

The original wild wheat has been selectively bred with other varieties to produce this modern bread wheat variety

1 Explain what the terms 'artificial selection' and 'selective breeding' mean.
2 Find out about the history of a favourite cat or dog variety. Describe the artificial selection and selective breeding programme which produced this variety.
3 Cats and dogs that win 'best of breed' titles are very valuable. If you owned a 'best of breed' dog how would you ensure that its offspring (pups) could win the title in the future?

5
Ideas of substance

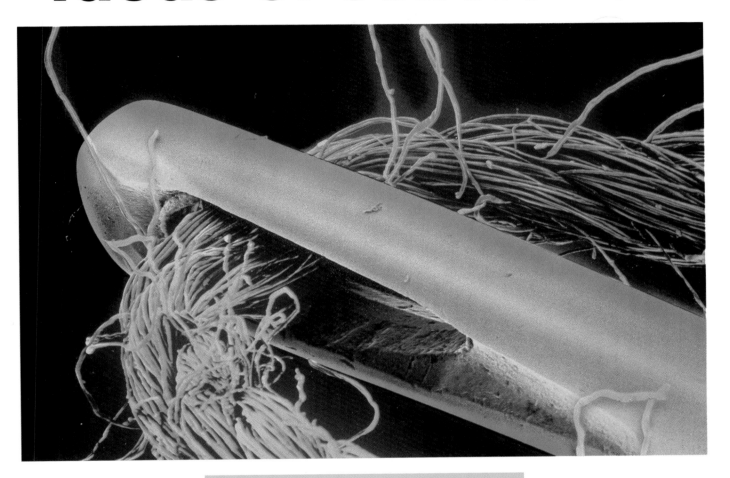

BIG IDEAS IN THIS UNIT

1 All atoms of the same element contain the same number of protons.
2 Elements are arranged in groups in the Periodic Table according to their similar chemical properties.
3 The valency, or combining power, of atoms is a help when working out chemical formulae.
4 Energy is released when atoms combine. More reactive atoms react to release more energy than less reactive atoms.
5 The reactivity series of metals is worked out by comparing the reactions of metals.

5.1 *The mighty (small) atom*

A Look at an atom

Atoms are so small that no one has actually seen one yet. There are electron micrographs (below) that show large molecules of millions of atoms all joined together. This is a bit like looking at a photo of the Great Wall of China taken from space, in that you can see the wall but each individual stone is too small to spot from such a distance.

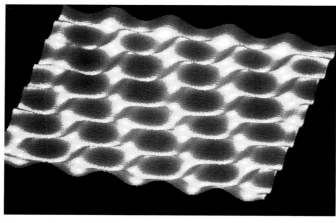

The surface of a sample of graphite, revealing the regular pattern of individual carbon atoms

The Great Wall of China

Scientists have studied the behaviour of atoms since 400 BC when Greek philosophers first suggested that the world was composed of small lumps of substances, each single one too small to see.

Our modern theory is built from the results of experiments conducted during the last 200 years. We cannot see an atom, we can only imagine what it looks like by thinking about its behaviour.

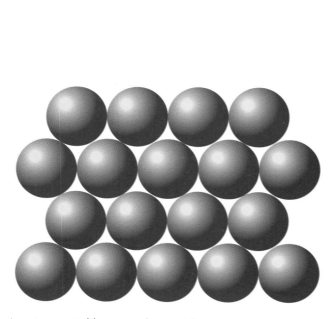

An atom acts like a single particle

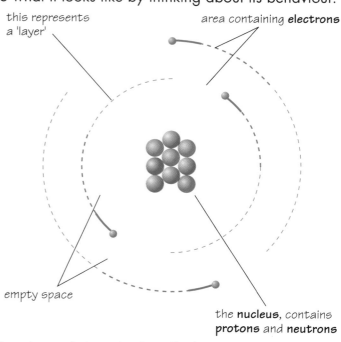

this represents a 'layer'

area containing **electrons**

empty space

the **nucleus**, contains **protons** and **neutrons**

but also as if it's made of smaller bits

According to this model, a lump of material, like bone, is made of substances that are in turn made of atoms. These atoms are mainly empty space!

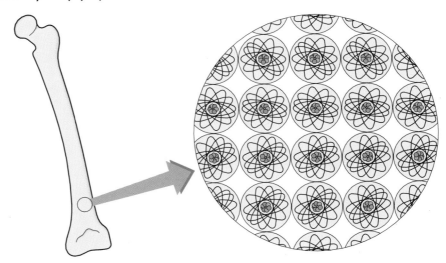

There are about 112 different kinds of atoms. Each one kind is a separate **element**. A piece of an element like gold will contain millions of gold atoms. In a similar way, one gram of pure iron contains millions of iron atoms. Steel is not an element, it is an alloy containing iron atoms and carbon atoms, and maybe other metal atoms too, like chromium and manganese.

pure iron

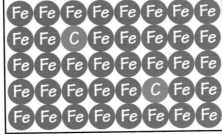

steel

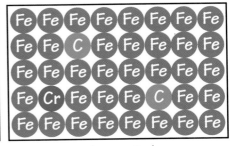

chrome steel

How can these tiny atoms be different? It helps to think of stones or bricks. Bricks do the same job (they join with others to make the wall), and they are made of the same kinds of substances. However, you can mix the ingredients in different ways and amounts to make different kinds of brick. Put these together and you get different kinds of walls.

Atoms contain the same kinds of ingredients

- protons
- neutrons
- electrons.

Look at the drawings below. See if you can spot how these same ingredients can result in different atoms.

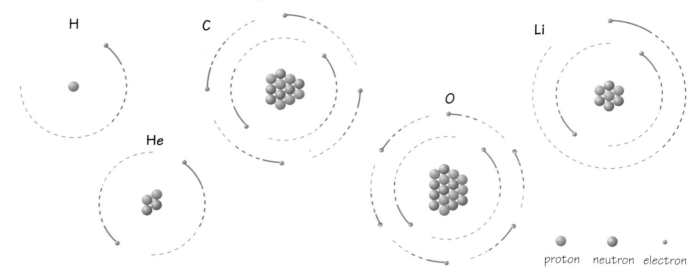

proton   neutron   electron

 Write the title *The mighty (small) atom* in your book. Make notes including these key points

- The size of atoms
  (Draw a labelled diagram of an atom too.)
- Elements and atoms
- Differences between atoms of different elements.

Collect

- Chunk of iron
- Chunk of carbon
- Electronic balance

Calculate the mass of an atom as follows.

a Find the mass of each chunk of the element. These chunks contain about 10^{22} atoms (that's ten thousand million million million atoms).
b Calculate the mass of one atom by division.

 1 Write a brief report about what you did.
2 Copy and complete the following table, using the drawings of these atoms above to help.

Atom	Number of protons	Number of electrons
H		
He		
Li		
C		

3 a Use a data book to work out how many protons the following atoms have

N	Cl	Na
O	Br	Cu
F	I	Fe.

b Which number did you use to work out the number of protons in the nucleus of these atoms?

B Connections

Scientific ideas are connected. The spider diagram shows some of these connections. It is only partly completed.

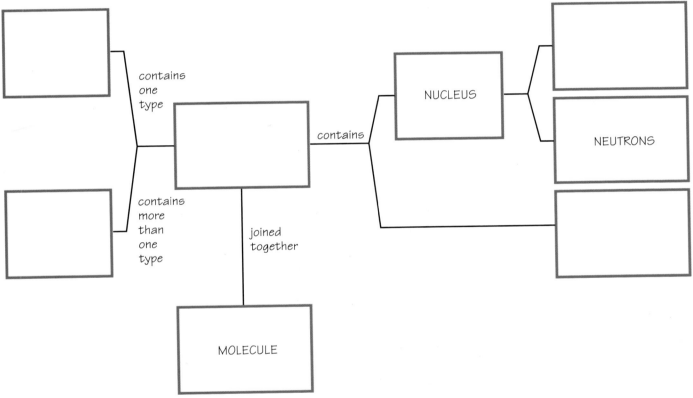

4 Copy and complete the spider diagram.

5 Draw a ladder of size with six rungs.

a Write the following labels on the ladder of size

- compound
- element
- proton
- atom
- neutron
- molecule
- electron.

b Look the sizes up in your data book and add these figures to the ladder.

5.2 *Family likeness*

A Groups of elements

The Periodic Table arranges all the known elements

- in order of increasing **atomic number** – 1 then 2 then 3 and so on
- in families, called **groups** – the reactive metals are together and so on.

You can see both these features below.

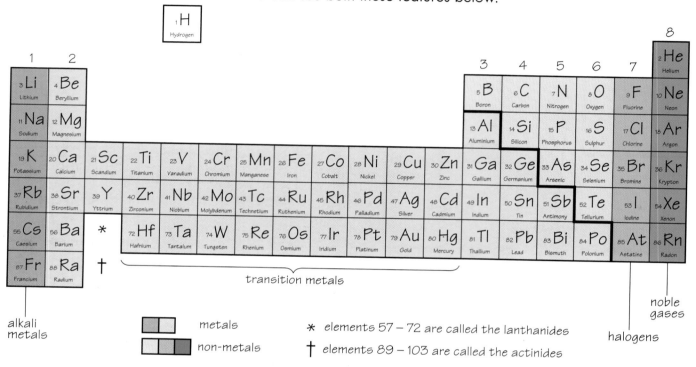

transition metals

alkali metals

noble gases

halogens

metals		
non-metals		

* elements 57 – 72 are called the lanthanides

† elements 89 – 103 are called the actinides

Group 1 is called the **alkali metals**. The first two members of this group are lithium and sodium. Your teacher may show you some unusual properties of alkali metals.

Write the title *Families of elements* in your book. Make notes including these key points

- How elements are arranged in the Periodic Table
- Properties of the alkali metals.

You are going to work as part of a group – a team of people with a similar research task. Your task is to find out as much as you can about **one** of the following groups of elements

- group 7 – the halogens
- group 8 (also called group 0) – the noble gases.

You can make use of any of the following (your teacher will tell you what is available)

a classroom textbooks
b wall posters
c the knowledge of members of staff (you will only be able to interview each person for two minutes so prepare your questions carefully)
d a computer database.

For your chosen group of elements

1 Give the family name and explain why these elements are all in the same group of the Periodic Table.
2 Write a paragraph about your team's research. Include

- the names of the elements in the group
- some of the 'family resemblances' that you discovered
- some of the uses of members of this group.

B Similarities

Elements in the same group of the Periodic Table will have similar properties. As you move down each group some properties change gradually – they are similar but *not* identical.

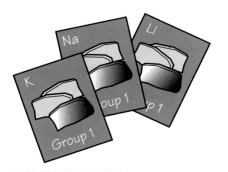

Collect

- Data sheet

Match the data sheet descriptions with the pictures above. Record your results in a two-column table with the headings **Symbol** and **Data number**.

3 How are elements grouped together in the Periodic Table?
4 Write a data file for caesium (group 1), astatine (group 7) and krypton (group 8).

5.3 *Joining atoms*

A Valency

Atoms join to form structures called either molecules or networks. The chemical formula of a substance is a shorthand way of writing how many atoms of one element combine with how many atoms of another within these structures.

means that a molecule of hydrogen contains 2 atoms of hydrogen joined together

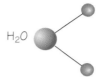

means that a molecule of water contains 2 atoms of hydrogen joined to 1 atom of oxygen

The combining power of each atom is known as its **valency**. Think of the valency as the number of hands that each atom has to hold on to another atom.

 valency of 1    valency of 2    valency of 3

Collect

- A set of valency cards

Find out the names of other atoms that have a valency of 1, 2 or 3. (Keep the cards for the next activity.)

The idea of valency can help us to work out some chemical formulae. For example, calcium chloride is calcium joined to chlorine (the *ide* part of the name means *only*). Calcium has a valency of 2 and chlorine has a valency of 1. Use the calcium and chlorine valency cards to follow the diagram below.

choose the cards

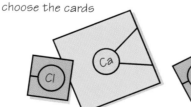  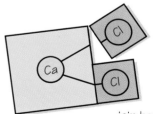

join bonds

To complete the formula you need one calcium to two chlorines. The formula for calcium chloride is

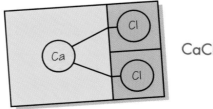 $CaCl_2$

Write the title *Joining atoms* in your book. Make notes including these key points

- Chemical formula
  (Give an example and explain what it means.)
- Valency
  (Explain what it means.)
- Draw several atoms to show their valency number
- Valency cards.
  (Illustrate how they can be used to work out the formula for magnesium fluoride.)

 1 Use the valency cards to work out and draw the valency picture for

- sodium chloride
- sodium sulphide
- calcium oxide
- hydrogen chloride
- magnesium chloride
- nitrogen hydride
- phosphorus bromide
- copper sulphide

- argon
- carbon hydride
- aluminium fluoride
- fluorine
- nitrogen
- magnesium nitride
- aluminium oxide
- carbon oxide.

2 Write the formula of the substance beside each of your valency pictures.

B More chemical formulae

All substances have chemical formulae, even common everyday substances like the ones below. From the formula, you should be able to work out what elements make up each substance. You may even be able to work out the chemical names of some of the substances.

salt $NaCl$ vinegar CH_3COOH water H_2O methane CH_4

sugar $C_{12}H_{22}O_{11}$ chalk $CaCO_3$ baking soda $NaHCO_3$ ammonia NH_3

gases mixed in the air N_2 O_2 CO_2 H_2O Ne Ar

Collect

- A set of labelled compounds

1 Examine the label.
2 Discuss each formula with a partner.
3 Work out all the elements present in it.

 Make a table of three columns to record the **Name**, **Formula** and **Names of elements present in**

a three common household substances
b all the substances that you examined in class.

5.4 Patterns in reactivity

A Energy and reactions

Energy is released when atoms combine.

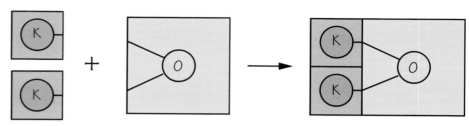

Different atoms will release different amounts of energy. For example, different metals can be burned in oxygen and the reactions compared. Metals can be listed according to their reactivity.

This order of reactivity explains why people began to use different metals at different times in history. Silver and gold have been known since ancient times. They are unreactive metals, which do not combine easily with other elements. On the other hand, more reactive metals like iron are only found in compounds, that is joined to other elements. The metal has to be pulled away from the other elements by using energy. Such metals were discovered only when people developed very hot furnaces. The most reactive metals form compounds so well that a great deal of energy is needed to break the join to separate out the metal. This energy can be supplied in the form of electricity and/or heat.

Molten sodium – the result of electrolysis of sodium chloride

Iron is extracted from its ore in a blast furnace

Gold panned from alluvial deposits in Peru

Metals can be pulled out of their compounds (**extracted**) by using energy. The amount of energy depends on the metal. The more energy that was released when the compound was made, the more is needed to break up the compound again.

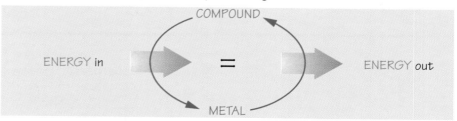

Write the title *Patterns in reactivity* in your book. Make notes including these key points

- The different reactivity of metals with oxygen
- The link between reactivity and energy released
- Order of reactivity
  (Explain what it means.)
- The reactivity series.
  (Stick a copy of the reactivity series into your notes at this point and predict the missing dates of discovery.)

Collect

- Bottles of:
  magnesium,
  aluminium,
  zinc, iron,
  tin, copper,
  dilute acid
- Anything else
  you need
- Safety
  glasses

Your task is to investigate the reactivity series using the metals from magnesium to copper in the series. Find out if the same pattern is observed when the metals react with dilute acid.

Hints

- Use a small amount of each metal each time.
- Decide in advance how many metals to test.
- **Measure** the reactivity using a thermometer.
- Decide which other **variables** to **control** for a fair comparison.

1 Write a report about your investigation.
2 Describe how you would improve your investigation if you had more time.

B Push off

The metal can also be 'pushed out' of compounds by using a more reactive metal. This is called **displacement**. Your teacher may show you how the iron in a nail can displace copper from solution.

Collect

- Spotting tile
- Solutions A
  and B (one is
  zinc nitrate,
  the other
  silver nitrate)
- Pieces of
  metals
- Safety
  glasses

1 Fill one line of dimples with solution A and another line with solution B.
2 Add a piece of one metal to a dimple in each line. Repeat for other metals, e.g. magnesium, iron and copper.
3 Decide which dimples show evidence of a chemical reaction (displacement). Record your results like this.

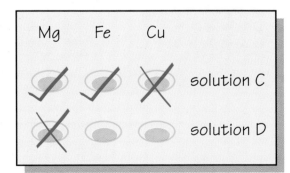

3 Explain what is meant by *displacement*.
4 Describe your experiment, including a sketch of your results.
5 Look at the reactivity series of metals. Find silver and zinc. Now find all the metals that you added to the two solutions. Which solution (A or B) is silver nitrate, which is zinc nitrate? Explain.

5.5 Moving ions

A Metal ions

Reactive metals are extracted from their compounds by using a lot of energy.

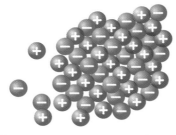

Heat or water separates the particles in the compound. The particles are atoms with an electrical charge and are called **ions**

The electricity causes the ions to move. The ions form atoms (or sometimes molecules) at the electrodes. The whole process is called **electrolysis**

Collect

- Filter paper
- Potassium iodide solution
- 2 connecting leads
- Crocodile clips
- Power supply (6 V d.c.)
- Safety glasses
- Solutions of tin bromide zinc iodide copper chloride
- Small beaker with 2 carbon rods

Electrical writing
1 Set up the circuit as in **a**.
2 Move the end of the free (red) lead over the surface of the filter paper and write your name.

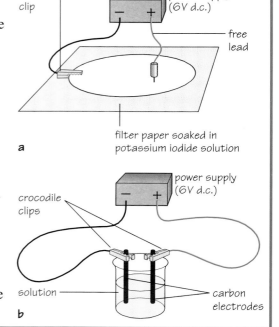

a

Which way?
1 Set up the circuit as in **b**.
2 Chose **one** of the solutions. Find out which electrode, + (red) or − (black), the metal ion moves to.
3 Choose another solution and again find out which electrode the metal moves to.
4 Write down a hypothesis about the movement of the metal ion and then use the third solution to check your ideas.

b

1 What do the words *ion* and *electrolysis* mean?
2 Draw a labelled diagram of one of your electrolysis experiments. Show clearly what evidence there was of a chemical reaction.
3 Was your hypothesis about the movement of the metal ion supported by your results? Explain.
4 A charged ion is always attracted to the electrode with the opposite charge. From your experimental results, what charge do you think
   a a metal ion has
   b a non-metal ion has?
   Explain your answers.

B Coloured ions

Some ions are coloured. We can use this fact to show that ions move towards the oppositely charged electrode during electrolysis.

These solutions contain blue copper ions.

These solutions contain yellow chromate ions.

Copper sulphate solution

Potassium chromate solution

Copper ammonium sulphate solution

Sodium chromate solution

Collect

- U-tube containing copper chromate solution in agar gel
- Vinegar
- 2 carbon electrodes
- Crocodile clips
- Power supply (12 V d.c.)
- Coloured pencils
- Safety glasses

1 Set up this experiment.
2 Predict what will happen in the experiment. (**Hint:** Think about the colour and attraction of the ions involved.)
3 Draw a coloured diagram to show the result that you expect.
4 Look at the result after 15 minutes.

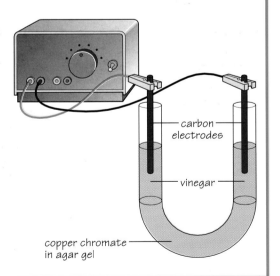

carbon electrodes

vinegar

copper chromate in agar gel

5 Describe your experiment. Did your results support your prediction?
6 Write down a likely explanation for the results of the experiment. Compare your explanation with those of others in the class.

5.6 *Problem*

Pipes for plumbing

Reactive metals are useless for carrying water since the metal and water react, as the following word equation shows

active metal +   water   →   metal hydroxide (an alkali)   + hydrogen

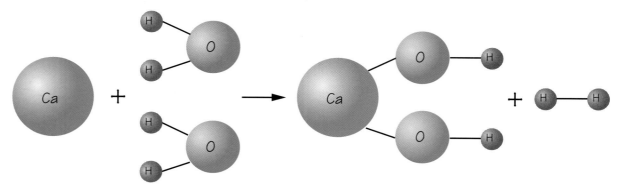

However, not all metals react with water. Some, like copper, can be used in plumbing.

Roman lead piping

Collect

- Piece of calcium from the teacher
- Boiling tube of water
- Universal indicator
- Wooden splint
- Safety glasses

Collect

- Magnesium ribbon
- Anything else you need

Set up the apparatus as shown below. Use the indicator solution and the splint to show that an alkali (calcium hydroxide) and hydrogen are the products of the reaction.

Magnesium is less reactive than calcium. Design and carry out an investigation to find out if it can be used to make water pipes.

Hints
- Think about the reactivity series of metals.
- Roman pipes lasted for over 1000 years. The metal had no reaction with the water.
- Even a slow reaction would be dangerous.
- Gas can be collected.

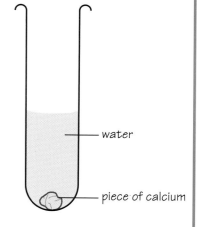

— water

— piece of calcium

  Write a report about your investigation.

5.7 *Talkabout*

Trail blazer

Chemical reactions occur in real life. You can see evidence of chemicals and chemical reactions in and around your school. Your group's task is to design and map out a *Chemistry trail*. This will be similar to a nature trail, but it will teach people something about the reactions around them.

This is an example of a nature trail. Look at it carefully.

Collect

• A map of the school area

Discuss the task in a group.

1 Decide which chemicals and chemical reactions will be good points of interest on your trail.

2 On a map of the school area, mark all the points of interest.

3 Together make up and print a guide sheet (perhaps on a word processor) which describes each of the points of interest on the trail.

Hints Include examples of

• elements, mixtures and compounds in use
• unusual substances that can be closely inspected
• metals in use and metal corrosion
• reactions actually happening
• evidence of chemical pollution.

Your methods could include

• asking questions to help people learn from the trail
• giving people something to do; for example, inspecting something with a hand lens or testing a liquid with pH paper.

Don't make the trail too long or too short; aim for a walk of about 15–20 minutes.

5.8 Readabout

Dalton's atomic symbols

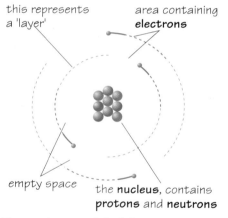

this represents a 'layer'

area containing **electrons**

empty space

the **nucleus**, contains **protons** and **neutrons**

The nuclear model of the atom

Atomic models

Scientific ideas can change, and they can also cause change. A good example is the theory of the atom. What do you think an atom is? What does it look like? Has it got a colour or shape? Does it spin and wobble? What is it made of? Before you read on, draw, colour and label a picture of an atom to show how *you* imagine it.

An idea like 'the atom' takes many people and many years to develop. Around 400 BC, Greek philosophers suggested that the world was composed of lumps of material, each too small to see, swirling around in total emptiness. These 'atoms' were thought to be completely solid, impossible to cut up and always on the move. Your own drawing of an atom may be very like this ancient idea.

Indian thinkers around the tenth century AD suggested that each of four elements had their own indestructible atoms. These invisible atoms were thought to cause effects that people could see.

Our modern theory of the atom is built on experiments conducted since the seventeenth century by several important thinkers. For example, John Dalton (1766–1844) was largely responsible for the idea that atoms are rearranged during chemical reactions to form new substances. He developed symbols to illustrate this.

By the nineteenth century Dalton's solid billiard-ball type of atom was largely accepted. However, experiments conducted by many people in many different countries during the twentieth century have changed the theory again. By 1940 the international model of the atom could be represented like the drawing on the left.

This is the nuclear atom. The idea that an atom is made of even smaller bits (called 'subatomic particles') is very important. Nuclear energy and nuclear bombs are direct results of the nuclear theory of the atom.

Scientists are still at work today on the theory of the atom. New subatomic particles like quarks and hadrons have been discovered since 1940. It is certainly possible that a new revolutionary theory of the atom will cause great changes to the way *you* live.

1 Among the scientists who developed the nuclear model of the atom were Ernest Rutherford, Niels Bohr and James Chadwick. Find out some of the important things that **one** of these scientists did and write about your findings.
2 How has the nuclear theory of the atom made our lives different from the lives of people who lived in the nineteenth century?
3 What is your opinion of nuclear power and nuclear weapons?
4 A person who has not made a final decision about something is said to have 'an open mind'. What is the value of keeping 'an open mind' about scientific ideas?

6 Extending the sciences

BIG IDEAS IN THIS UNIT

1 The structure and properties of the substance DNA are key factors in understanding the biology of inheritance.

2 Much variation in human populations is caused by mixing the gene pool and by gene mutation.

3 The structure and properties of substances called alkanes are key factors in understanding the chemistry of mineral oil.

4 Chemical reactions can be represented by balanced chemical equations.

5 The theoretical descriptions of kinetic and potential energy are key factors in understanding the physics of energy efficiency.

6 Energy conservation and energy dissipation during energy transfers are described by two 'laws'.

6.1 *The biology of human inheritance*

A Theory

DNA

Life on Earth depends on genetic material to pass on information for building new individuals. For example, a fern plant inherits plans for its structure and its behaviour from its parent(s). It grows up to be a fern rather than a rose. A crocodile mother and father produce sperm and eggs that contain genetic material. Every cell in the body of the baby crocodile receives that information, which carries the instructions for making a crocodile. Genetic material is carried in the substance deoxyribonucleic acid (DNA).

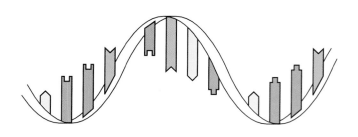

DNA is a large molecule, like a chain. Four different types of small branches stick out of the side of the main chain – these are known as **bases**. They are given the code letters A, C, T and G

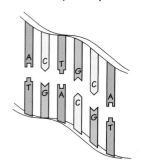

The bases attract and pair up with one another – A with T; C with G. This means that a strand of DNA usually pairs up with another strand to make a kind of ladder. Each 'rung' of the ladder consists of a **base pair**

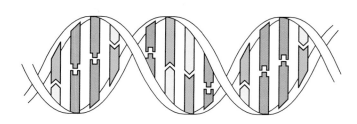

The double strand twists into a spiral, which is described as a **double helix**

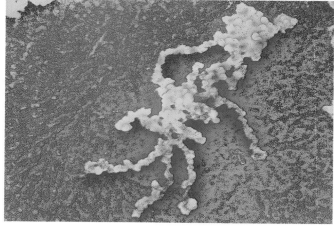

A **gene** may be made up of hundreds or thousands of base pairs. Together they give the code for building a particular protein molecule

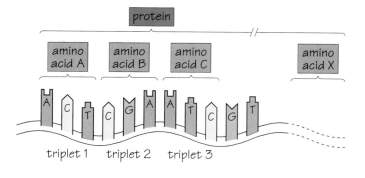

The DNA double helix can unravel. Each **triplet** of bases represents one amino acid. Amino acids join up, in the same order as the triplets, to make protein

The really amazing thing about DNA is that it can replicate itself. Again, the two strands 'unzip'. Each separate strand attracts the right bases to make the pairs again and so builds up a copy of the original double helix molecule.

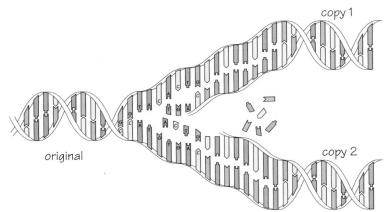

In this way, the DNA from your parents was copied and half of it was present in each of the two sex cells that joined at your conception, divided and then grew up to be you!

Mixing the gene pool

You look very different from your classmates. Thank goodness! The world would be a very boring place if everybody was exactly the same. Much (*but not all!*) of this variation is influenced by genetic inheritance – you are you mostly because of your parents.

In sexual reproduction the genetic material of both parents is mixed. Each child ends up with half the father's and half the mother's genes; which half is determined by a process that is largely random.

There are two genes for each characteristic in the fertilised egg – one from each parent

Over a long period of time, as each generation produces the next, the genetic material from many different families is mixed and mingled. The human gene pool is therefore constantly 'stirred' to make new and unique mixtures. This process is the major source of variation in the human population. When the gene pool is kept small, for example if a small section of the population decide only to marry each other, then genetic diseases become more likely.

Mutation

Over 50% of the 4000 or so known genetic diseases are caused by a change in the chemical structure of one single gene in one of the sex cells. Such a change is called a **mutation** and it will have occurred without any obvious sign.

Mutations in human sex cells are known to be caused by a range of environmental factors, including exposure to high-energy radiation and chemical attack by substances like environmental pollutants, drugs and cigarette smoke.

Things that cause mutations in sex cells may also change the DNA in other body cells causing them to grow uncontrollably and form a **cancer**.

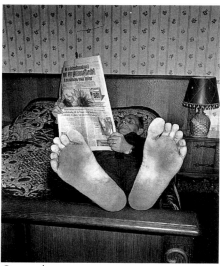

Count the toes

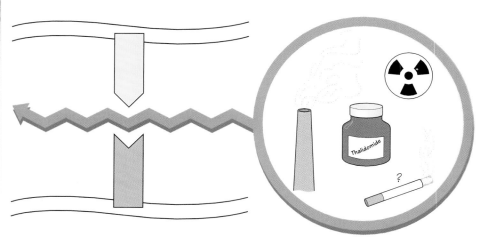

Many mutations are dangerous or even lethal to the life that begins when an egg is fertilised. The new individual may not be able to make a very important protein. This is like trying to build a house with incomplete or wrong building plans. Sometimes mutations are less harmful or have very little effect and occasionally they are actually helpful. For example, people with an alteration in a gene on a particular chromosome survive well but they have damaged haemoglobin in their red blood cells. This reduces the capacity of the blood cell to carry oxygen and in the homozygous situation (when both alleles have the alteration, see page 117) results in sickle cell anaemia. However, the malaria parasite cannot live easily inside the deformed red blood cells and so this mutation is helpful in many countries where malaria is prevalent, particularly in the heterozygous condition (when one allele is altered and the other is normal, see page 117).

Write a suitable title. Make notes under the following headings

- The structure and function of DNA
- The role of the gene pool
- Mutation, with examples.

Collect

- Genetic make-up cards

Work with a partner.

Shuffle the parents' genetic make-up cards and then divide them into two equal sets.

Each person takes one set, representing the genetic make-up of a child of these parents.

The cards with a ✓ will show up in the child; those with a ✗ will not.

Use your cards to complete the drawing of the child's face.

Compare your drawing with your partner's (a child from the same genetic pool).

male	female	female
X Y	X X	X X
colour-blind	carrier	colour-blind

● gene for red–green colour-blindness

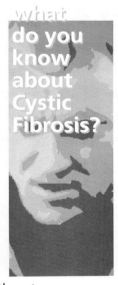

cystic fibrosis

B Research an inherited disease

Some conditions and diseases are partly caused by a mutation, where the mutated gene builds an altered protein that cannot do its proper job in the body.

One example is red–green colour-blindness. The mutation is on the X chromosome and is therefore said to be **sex-linked**. It results in the person not being able to tell the difference between red and green; both colours look the same. A woman has two X chromosomes and the damaged gene must be present on both for the woman to be colour-blind. A man has only one X chromosome and so the condition is more common in males. Another sex-linked disease is haemophilia.

Three important inherited diseases (not necessarily sex-linked) are

haemophilia

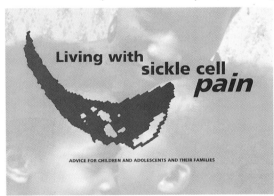

sickle cell anaemia

Research one of the above diseases. Find out the symptoms, the cause and the treatment usually prescribed. More importantly, try to discover how people with the disease manage to lead a fairly 'normal' life.

Use the information to build up a research file on the disease. Use the hints to help you.

Hints

- Look for basic information in encyclopedias and similar sources (books, CD-ROMs).
- Look for more detailed medical information by doing a key word search in your local library or on a database (or the Internet).
- Send off for human-interest material to the charity/research trust that specialises in the disease.
- Ask your doctor for information.

6.2 The chemistry of mineral oil

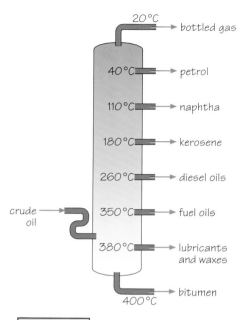

20°C → bottled gas
40°C → petrol
110°C → naphtha
180°C → kerosene
260°C → diesel oils
350°C → fuel oils
380°C → lubricants and waxes
crude oil
400°C → bitumen

A Theory

What is crude oil?

Oil is a black liquid, sometimes thin, sometimes thick (**viscous**), which is present underground in places that used to be covered by ocean waters. Each type of crude oil contains many different compounds, mixed in varying amounts depending on the place where the oil is found. Oil is a fossil fuel, which means that it was made many millions of years ago by the action of high temperatures and pressures on the bodies of dead sea creatures. Bodies contain carbon compounds and so it is not surprising to find carbon compounds in crude oil.

Separating crude oil

The mixture of compounds is heated until it boils. The vapour is then cooled down gradually in a **fractionating tower**. Substances with different boiling points change from gas back into liquid at different temperatures.

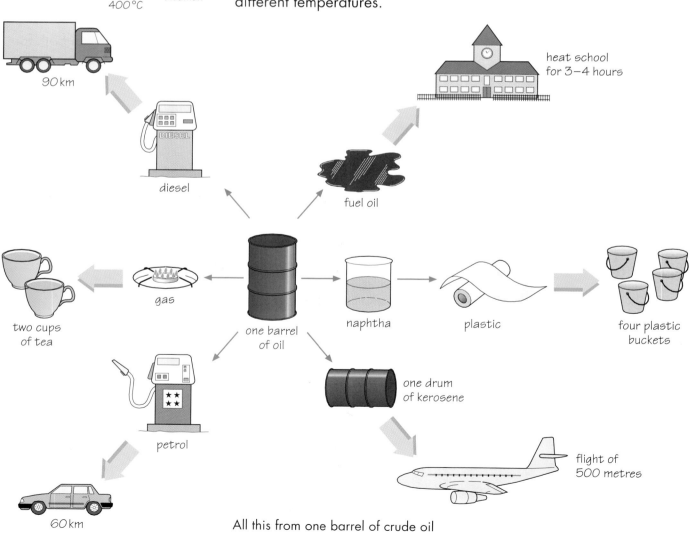

90 km

heat school for 3–4 hours

diesel

fuel oil

two cups of tea

gas

one barrel of oil

naphtha

plastic

four plastic buckets

petrol

one drum of kerosene

60 km

flight of 500 metres

All this from one barrel of crude oil

Different boiling points

When a substance boils, its molecules move faster and faster until they have enough kinetic energy to separate. The bigger the molecule, the more energy it needs to move away from its neighbours. So, substances with big molecules have higher boiling points than those with smaller molecules. This link is obvious when you inspect the boiling points of the **alkanes**, a family of compounds present in crude oil. The molecules of these compounds all have a similar structure and general molecular formula, but they differ in their size.

	methane	ethane	propane	butane	pentane
structure	$H-\underset{\overset{\displaystyle H}{|}}{\overset{\overset{\displaystyle H}{|}}{C}}-H$	H—C—H H—C—H	H—C—H H—C—H H—C—H	H—C—H H—C—H H—C—H H—C—H	H—C—H H—C—H H—C—H H—C—H H—C—H
formula of the molecule	CH_4	C_2H_6	C_3H_8	C_4H_{10}	C_5H_{12}
boiling point in °C	−162	−87	−42	−0.5	36

Combustion of alkanes

The alkanes are a series of **hydrocarbon** compounds with a similar structure. The general molecular formula of the alkanes is

$$C_nH_{2n+2}$$
(where n is the number of carbon atoms in the molecule)

During combustion, the atoms in the alkane will react with oxygen atoms, forming oxides. Heat energy will be released.

The simplest alkane is methane, which makes up about 96% of natural gas. Paraffin and candle wax both contain alkanes. Each of these substances will form the same two combustion products – can you work out what they are?

Write a suitable title. Make notes under the following headings

- The origin of crude oil
- The useful substances present in crude oil
- The method used to separate crude oil into fractions
- The structure of the alkanes
  (Give at least four examples.)
- The combustion of alkanes.
  (Include your prediction of which two substances are produced when any alkane burns.)

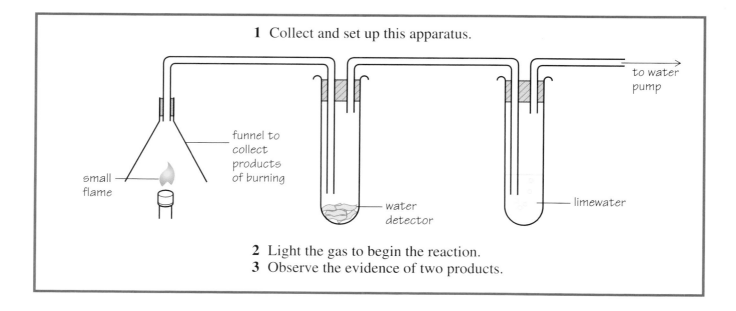

1 Collect and set up this apparatus.

to water pump

funnel to collect products of burning

small flame

water detector

limewater

2 Light the gas to begin the reaction.
3 Observe the evidence of two products.

1 What were the products of the combustion reaction?
2 Write a word equation for this reaction.
3 Write a symbol equation for the reaction

Balancing an equation

During any chemical interaction, the atoms are rearranged. Therefore all the atoms that make up the reactants must end up in the products. We will use the example of the combustion of methane to explore this idea.

Collect

- A molecular modelling kit

1 Make a model of one molecule of each reactant and each product in the burning reaction.

$$CH_4 \text{ and } O_2 \rightarrow CO_2 \text{ and } H_2O$$
reactants   products

2 Lay your models out in the same order as above.

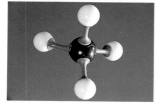

methane

oxygen

carbon dioxide

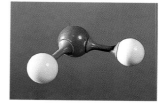

water

3 Have all the atoms in the reactants been used up in the products? If not, we say that the equation is **not balanced**. Build more models of any reactant and/or product molecule and try to balance it.

Collect

• A balancing act worksheet

4 The balanced symbol equation is

$$CH_4 + 2O_2 \rightarrow CO_2 + 2H_2O$$

These numbers are for balancing.
They mean that 2 molecules are needed.

5 On the worksheet balance the symbol equations by multiplying some of the formulae in each equation.

Correct the examples yourself and stick the sheet into your book.

B Research substances from oil

Crude oil is the origin of many substances that we use every day – nylon, paint, plastics, medicines and some cosmetics are all produced using oil. Your teacher may show you some others.

All of these objects are made from substances obtained from oil

Research one of these substances. Find out about the chemical properties and the uses of the substance and something about how it is produced in industry. Use the information to build up a research file about the substance.

6.3 *The physics of energy efficiency*

A Theory

Energy

Events in the world are usually accompanied by a transfer of energy. Some teachers have likened energy to money. Like energy, money is often needed in our world to enable things to happen. Like energy, the money is transferred and an event takes place. And again like energy, the money isn't part of the event in any physical sense; the painter paints your house because he/she is paid but the notes aren't used to splash the paint on! Finally, like energy, the amount of money before and after the event is the same; it is conserved even though it will end up in a different pocket.

householder

transfer
of
cash

painter

potential
energy

transfer
of
energy

kinetic
energy

You have come across different forms of energy in science. These forms are really just different disguises that energy takes when it is transferred. Scientists now argue that all forms of energy can be worked out to be *either* **kinetic energy** (the energy associated with movement) *or* **potential energy** (the energy associated with stored forms of energy).

Kinetic energy

Movement energy is obviously kinetic.

So too is *heat energy*. Heat is caused by the kinetic movement of particles. The more the particles move about, the more energy they have and the hotter the object appears to be.

Sound energy is also linked to movement; in this case vibrating particles transfer the sound.

Potential energy

Potential energy takes different disguises too.

Gravitational energy exerts a force field on objects and causes them to change height. We say that an object that is up high has gained stored gravitational energy. This is entirely due to the increased effect of the potential field.

Electrical energy also exerts a force field on objects; those that carry a charge are affected. So charged ions move towards an oppositely charged electrode. The potential energy is transferred through the electric field.

Indeed all *chemical interactions* are really the result of the interacting electrical fields of the atoms involved. Potential energy operates in a battery at the level of electrons and other particles in the atoms.

Light, and other radiated energy, is transferred by *electromagnetic waves*, a form of potential energy, which is again related to the operation of a field.

Finally, even the stored energy in springy and elastic substances can be shown to be caused by the molecules' electric fields, and so this is really another form of electrical potential energy.

Energy conservation – the first law

Energy is described in physics by several laws. These laws are statements that scientists have not been able to disprove in spite of many attempts to do so. The first law states that after a change the amount of energy is the same as it was before the change. If this law is always true then energy cannot be created nor destroyed, just moved somewhere else.

This first law is about the **conservation** of energy.

Energy dispersal – the second law

This second law concerns energy transfer and states that energy is always spread out more after an event. This affects us because when we try to transfer energy some of it will always escape, usually by becoming waste heat. For example, when you pedal your bike some of the energy from your body is transferred to heat up the road and the surrounding air.

The second law is about the **dispersal (dissipation)** of energy.

pedal your bicycle

heat (dissipated)

movement

sound (dissipated)

Efficiency

When energy is dissipated it becomes more difficult for people to use. Think of the motor car. Some of the potential energy from the fuel is transferred into the kinetic energy of the wheels. However, some is wasted because it is transferred to kinetic energy throughout the car (sound vibrations) and to kinetic energy of the surrounding molecules (heating the engine parts, the air and the road). Hence, the overall efficiency of the motor car is only about 15%.

Write a suitable title. Make notes under the following headings

- The many disguises of kinetic and potential energy
- The first and second law of energy
- The low energy efficiency of the motor car.

B Research ways of saving energy

There are many ways of saving energy in the home. Familiar methods (such as double glazing, draughtproofing and cavity wall insulation) reduce the transfer of heat energy from the home to the surroundings. An appliance like a heat pump concentrates heat energy, so that previously wasted heat can be reused (there is a heat pump inside every fridge). Installations such as wind farms and solar power stations capture energy that would otherwise end up as so much more hot air.

Wind turbines

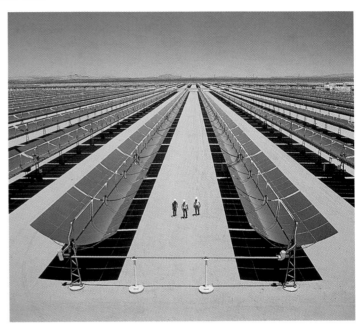

A solar power station

You are going to research ways of saving energy. You should try to find out about recent technology that is being tested for use in either the home or the town. Use the information to build up a research file.

Hints
- Look for basic information in a *recent* encyclopedia or CD-ROM. (Check and record the publication date.)
- Look for more detailed information by doing a keyword search.
- Contact companies, government agencies and groups that are working in the field of research for answers to specific questions which you have worked out in advance.
- Ask your local energy provider for information.

6.4 Problem

Some examples of animals with good heat insulation

Pet insulation

Animals (for example, pet guinea pigs) get heat energy from the respiration of food molecules. The more heat the animal loses, the more food it has to use up. If the animal loses too much heat then it could become ill and might even die. So heat energy is valuable and should not be wasted. Many animals are well insulated to keep the heat energy inside their bodies.

Humans have some insulation too but it is not efficient enough. So we have designed and used materials to help keep heat inside our bodies and also inside our houses. We can use this technology to help our pets keep warm too.

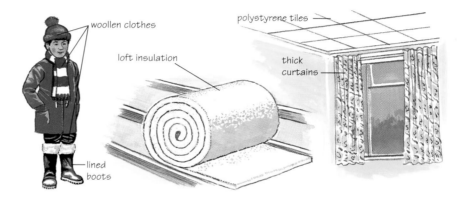

Some examples of objects with good heat insulation

Collect

- Samples of materials
- Thermometer
- Anything else you need

Use your general knowledge and the pictures above to find the best material for insulating a guinea pig's hutch. You will have to design, plan and carry out an investigation into the insulating properties of suitable materials. Discuss the four areas illustrated below with your group.

If you are totally stuck then ask for help from your teacher.

a Compare **b** Control the variables **c** Measure **d** Record

Describe your investigation on a poster that covers the four areas given above. Each member of the group should produce a different section of the poster.

6.5 *Talkabout*

Nuclear radiation

Some substances are **radioactive**. This means that they contain unstable atoms that give out energy in the form of radiation. *Background radiation* is present all around us from natural sources, like granite rock. People also try to find *beneficial uses of radiation*. Great care has to be taken because *radiation can be harmful* if it is not controlled properly.

The phrases in *italics* are the titles of three talks. Your group will be given one title. The group has to plan and record a three-minute talk about the **facts** behind the phrase. You can make use of any resources that you can think of. The panels below give you some hints.

How to illustrate a talk

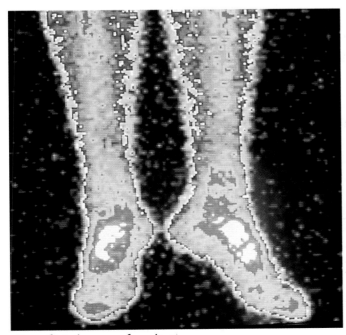

Beneficial uses of radiation

Background radiation

Radiation can be harmful

The day the lizards were stoned to death

THE DINOSAURS went out like a light. The end came like a bolt from the blue. About 65 million years ago the world was a hot, wet, leafy place and trees grew in the Antarctic and on Greenland and the huge, ferocious tyrannosaurus rex and the bland and bovine brontosaur, the megalosaur, pterosaur and icthyosaur contentedly plodded or paddled or swam in a cold-blooded sort of way over most of the globe.

Then one day, they were gone. If the scientists are right (and they don't agree among themselves) the end was so sudden it literally *was* a bolt from the blue: a huge, thumping asteroid from outer space that was five miles across, weighed 500 billion tons and hit our world at 25 miles a second with an earth-shaking splat.

How do we know? Geologists can read the Earth like a book. It is really a book, written by time. Chapter one is the oldest rocks we know, and sometimes the deepest, and most of us are actually standing on the last page to be written.

Just as one day future geologists will be able to reconstruct our lives from old cigarette packets, aluminium ring pulls and fossil chewing gum so geologists can put together a picture of the past at a particular time from the rocks themselves, the air trapped in them and the debris of ancient life – leaves, spiders, amber, dinosaur droppings, teeth, bones, pollen and so on – trapped in fossil form forever.

If it is a book, some of the pages are torn out and others are scrumpled and scribbled over so sometimes it's a matter of following the story as far as chapter five and then landing yourself in chapter seven and guessing what happened in between, or combing the world for another paragraph, or a torn half page.

When the geologists were reading the chapter called the Cretaceous, the last chapter of the dinosaurs, however, they found a last sentence. And then the chapter called the Tertiary began, with a completely different story with new characters in it: none of them dinosaurs. And right there in the last sentence they think they have found a very short account of what some of them have called the 'worst weekend in the history of the world'.

Bolts from the blue happen every day. Most meteorites are pretty small, and burn up in the atmosphere. At night we call them 'shooting stars'. But every now and then a bigger one lands with a thud somewhere. And every few million years there is a really big one.

So what happened at the end of the Cretaceous? When a visitor five miles across weighing 500 billion tons and travelling at 25 miles a second hits even something as thin as air, it's like a bomb exploding against a brick wall, only much worse.

At 20 miles up it would have heated the air to 2000 degrees and set the nitrogen and the oxygen aflame. This would have turned into a boiling sheet of millions of tons of nitric acid. Then the asteroid would have hit the sea – it must have been the sea because nobody has found a 65 million year old crater big enough – and boiled it, started a tidal wave five miles high then pulverised itself into dust which shot up 20 miles.

This dust would have circled round the stratosphere and blotted out the sun for three months. Dinosaurs were cold blooded. They had to have sun to keep alive. The plants they ate would have died, because plants need sun. The world would have turned terribly cold, so cold, so suddenly it freeze-dried all the trees. Which means that the next lightning storm would have set them aflame.

Geologists poking about in the debris of the meteorite, right there, everywhere in the world, at the last sentence of the Cretaceous, have found so much soot they think that 80 per cent of all the trees in the world would have burned in one vast planet-wide inferno.

So when it wasn't freezing it would have been burning, and when it wasn't burning, there would have been a deadly rain of corroding acid. Even more (this sounds like overkill!) the acid rain would have leached mercury, lead, cadmium and arsenic from the rocks and into the streams to poison the fresh water. And the asteroid would have blasted so much limestone into smithereens it would have increased the carbon dioxide content of the air. It also would have destroyed the ozone layer.

So think about it. First the dinosaurs near the asteroid would have been pulverised in the collision, or fried in the heat flash, or swept away by a tidal wave. The survivors would have frozen almost instantly to death. Or starved. Or they would have burned in forest fires or been gassed or poisoned by acid rain. And anything that crept out when the skies cleared would have suffocated in a greenhouse earth and got skin cancer from the ultraviolet light normally blocked by the ozone layer.

That last sentence turned into a death sentence, and for some animals, the world came, right there and then, to a full stop.

Tim Radford in the *Guardian*,
20 September 1989

1 What do some scientists think happened on 'the worst weekend in the history of the world'?
2 What effects did this have on the atmosphere?
3 **a** Why might the plants have burned?
  b Is there any evidence that plants did burn?
4 Read the paragraph before the last again and list five things that could have caused the death of the dinosaurs.
5 What do you think about the scientific hypothesis given in the passage?
6 **a** Discuss with your classmates other possible reasons for the end of the dinosaurs. (Do not worry about your ideas being wrong. Many scientists think that the hypothesis of the meteorite is wrong.)
  b Research your best idea using printed or electronic reference material. Write a short article about your research findings.

Extensions

Manufacturing plant

Green plants make their own food by photosynthesis. The food is the simple sugar glucose. Plants use glucose as the starting point for the manufacture of all the other compounds they need to grow and survive. Some of these are shown below.

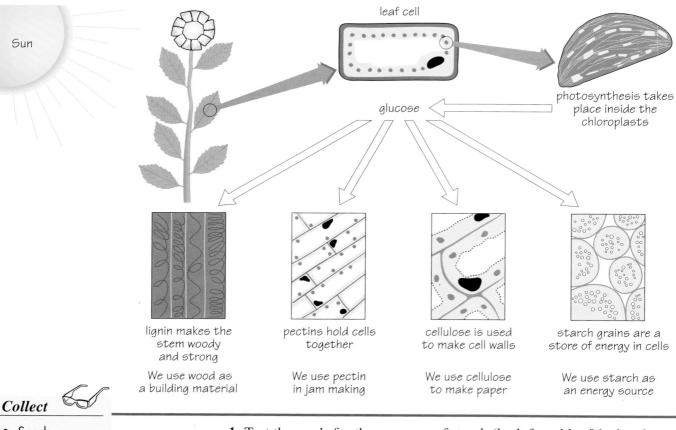

Sun

leaf cell

photosynthesis takes place inside the chloroplasts

glucose

lignin makes the stem woody and strong

We use wood as a building material

pectins hold cells together

We use pectin in jam making

cellulose is used to make cell walls

We use cellulose to make paper

starch grains are a store of energy in cells

We use starch as an energy source

Collect

- Seeds
- Iodine solution
- Plant stem material
- Potato
- Scalpel
- Microscope
- Microscope slides
- Safety glasses

1 Test the seeds for the presence of starch (look for a blue/black colour with iodine).
2 Prepare a microscope slide of a thin slice of potato tissue. Stain this with iodine.
3 Prepare a microscope slide of the stem material.

1 Name four plant materials made from glucose. Explain why they are essential to the plant.
2 Make a table with suitable title and headings to show the results of your starch test on seeds.
3 Make a drawing of what you saw on each of your microscope slides.
    Label starch grains on the potato drawing.
    Label cellulose cell walls and lignin on the stem drawing.

The cycle of elements

There are around 90 naturally occurring elements. Many are required by living things in tiny amounts. However, four major elements are required to form the tissues of all living things. These are hydrogen, oxygen, carbon and nitrogen. For life on Earth to continue the available amounts of these essential elements must remain steady. They are recycled through the ecosystem.

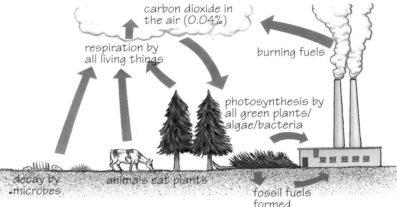

The carbon cycle

Carbon and oxygen are recycled and kept in balance by the processes of respiration and photosynthesis. The activities of humans seem to be upsetting the balance of this cycle. The consequences could be drastic.

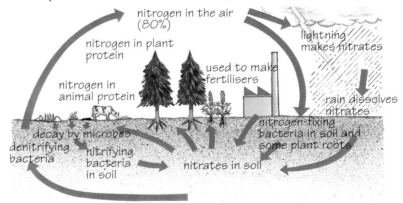

The nitrogen cycle

Nitrogen is recycled in a more complicated way, involving several different processes. The activities of humans may be upsetting this cycle too.

1 Collect and complete copies of the carbon and nitrogen cycles, and stick them into your book.

2 Describe how the activities of people are causing problems in

* the carbon cycle
* the nitrogen cycle.

3 What do you think could be done to
  a keep the amount of carbon dioxide in the air at a low level
  b keep enough nitrogen compounds in garden soil?

Rates of reaction

The rate of photosynthesis depends on several factors such as the availability of reactants, the light intensity and the temperature. Two systems can be used to study the rate of photosynthesis.

Counting bubbles

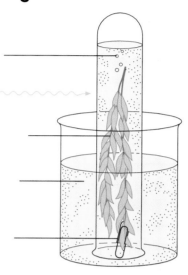

Canadian pond weed (*Elodea*) releases bubbles of oxygen from the cut end of the stem. The number of bubbles in 30 seconds or 1 minute gives an indication of the rate of photosynthesis

Colour change

before

after

water

bicarbonate indicator

bicarbonate indicator

If you bubble your breath through bicarbonate indicator solution it will turn yellow. The time it takes for the indicator to turn from yellow to orange/red gives an indication of the rate of photosynthesis. Finally, it turns purple

Think about which system to use to investigate the rate of photosynthesis. Think about the advantages and disadvantages of each before you choose.
    Carry out an investigation on *either*

- the effect of light intensity on the rate of photosynthesis *or*
- the effect of temperature on the rate of photosynthesis.

Design your investigation, show your plan to your teacher, and then collect the apparatus you need.

Write a report on your investigation under the following headings

- Aim
  (Which variable did you investigate? What was your hypothesis?)
- Method
  (Use labelled diagrams. Which variables were kept the same? How did you do this?)
- Results
  (Show your results in a table)
- Conclusion
- Experimental improvements.
  (What were the problems with the experimental system? What could you have done to make your results more reliable?)

Decomposers

Death and decay play an important part in the ecosystem. Uneaten food eventually rots. The soft remains of animals decay quickly; even the bones break up eventually. The photograph shows what happens to apples that are left on the tree for a few weeks.

Worms, slugs, fungi and bacteria bring about decomposition and decay. In warm, moist conditions this can happen very quickly. These decomposers return essential minerals and elements that plants need back to the soil. These essential minerals can then be passed on to other living organisms through food webs. They can be used again and again. This is called recycling.

A slug eating its way through a leaf

A mass of sulphur tuft fungi

Earthworms are important recyclers

Collect

- Grapes
- Test tubes
- Anything else you need

Humans often want to prevent the action of decomposers. Your task is to prevent the decomposition of some grapes. Grapes are full of useful food substances like sugar. Bacteria and fungi on the grapes' skins can use the sugars as an energy source and will rot the grapes.

Use your knowledge and the information above to stop the rot. Think of three or four different methods to prevent decay. Cut the grapes in half. Set up a control experiment – one grape cut in half, left in the open. You can compare the results of your methods against this.

Write a letter to the manager in charge of fruit and vegetables for a particular supermarket chain to advise him/her how to prevent grapes from rotting.

Explain what causes the grapes to rot and how your advice should prevent this from happening or at least delay it.

Environmental news

All over the world important habitats are being destroyed. This can happen for a number of reasons

- The local population may be increasing and so needs more land
- Natural resources such as water, timber and minerals may be found and exploited
- Natural disasters like floods, earthquakes and volcanoes can destroy habitats
- Human error can lead to major environmental disasters.

The Mount St Helens eruption in Washington, USA, destroyed hundreds of acres of forest

The wreck of a supertanker off the Alaskan coast badly damaged coastal wildlife

The good news is that ecosystems can recover. It might take time but with human help and protection it is possible.

Life returning to the Mount St Helens area

Alaskan wildlife is now recovering

1 Make a wall display of environmental issues from local and national newspapers.
2 Find examples of the environment under threat.
3 Find examples of good news for the environment.
4 Underline or circle any references to food chains or food webs in the articles you find.

Cooling and heating

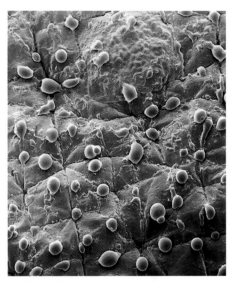

Coloured scanning electron micrograph of the skin surface showing sweat droplets (blue)

The human body cannot measure a wide range of temperatures but it does control its own internal temperature very accurately. Part of the brain called the hypothalamus acts like a thermostat. It takes information from temperature-sensing nerves in the skin and it measures the temperature of the blood flowing through it. When body temperature is higher or lower than normal a series of events is triggered that brings temperature back to 37°C. For example, when the temperature rises above normal

- there is no shivering
- blood passes to surface blood vessels where it loses heat
- skin hairs lower to enable heat to escape more easily
- there is increased sweating; when sweat evaporates skin temperature falls.

Body size has an important effect on the rate of cooling. When the body cools down the opposite events are triggered.

Collect

- 3 beakers (50, 100, 250 cm³)
- 3 temperature sensors
- Interfacing equipment
- Printer
  or
- 3 thermometers
- Graph paper
- Stop-clock

Investigate the rate of cooling from three beakers of different sizes. Predict which beaker will cool most quickly. Use hot water from the tap or ask your teacher for hot water from a kettle. The beakers should have water of the same temperature in them at the start of the experiment. If possible use temperature sensors and interface these with a computer to measure temperature change continuously over a 20-minute period. Print out the graph at the end of the experiment.

1 Calculate the surface area of each beaker. (**Hint:** calculate the area of the circular top and base plus the area of the cylindrical sides.)
2 You know the volume of each beaker. Calculate the ratio of the surface area to volume for each beaker.
3 Write a short report on your experiment. Include a graph of temperature against time. Explain the results in terms of the surface area to volume ratio of each beaker.
4 If the beakers were mammals describe the response they would make to cooling.
5 If you were designing a water-filled radiator to heat a room describe the features you would include to ensure it was an efficient heater.

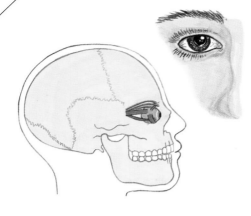

See here

Our eyes help us to make sense of the world. We see an object because **light is reflected from it** and enters the eye. The light is bent or **focused** onto the retina. Messages are then sent to the brain along the optic nerve. The brain 'sees' the object.

You may have the chance to dissect an eye. If you do, look carefully for the important structures shown below.

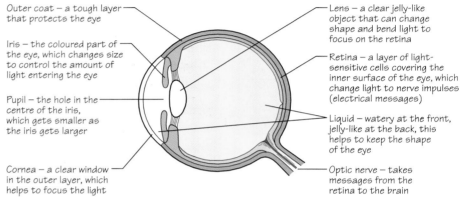

Outer coat – a tough layer that protects the eye

Iris – the coloured part of the eye, which changes size to control the amount of light entering the eye

Pupil – the hole in the centre of the iris, which gets smaller as the iris gets larger

Cornea – a clear window in the outer layer, which helps to focus the light

Lens – a clear jelly-like object that can change shape and bend light to focus on the retina

Retina – a layer of light-sensitive cells covering the inner surface of the eye, which change light to nerve impulses (electrical messages)

Liquid – watery at the front, jelly-like at the back, this helps to keep the shape of the eye

Optic nerve – takes messages from the retina to the brain

 Collect and complete an eye diagram sheet. Then decide which of the two investigations below to carry out.

Collect

- A set of experiment cards

Collect

- Tin can, ends removed
- Piece of black paper
- Piece of greaseproof paper
- 2 elastic bands
- Pin
- Glass rod
- Candle and matches
- Lenses

1 Complete the experiments with a partner. Answer the questions in your book.

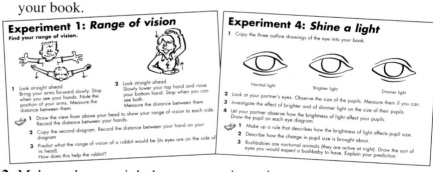

or 2 Make and use a pinhole camera to investigate

- the shape of an image on the retina
- the effect of pupil (hole) size on the image
- the effect of glasses (lenses) on the image.

Make labelled drawings to record your results.

screen = retina

Electromagnetic waves

Light consists of waves that have electric and magnetic energy which move through space to our eyes. These waves are called 'electromagnetic' waves, or **electromagnetic radiation**. The waves move forward at colossal speed – about 300 000 km/s.

There are different types of electromagnetic radiation, depending on the **wavelength** of the waves. Each type is produced and detected in its own way, and has a different effect on our bodies. The wavelengths vary over a wide range. The picture shows them spread out according to their wavelength into an electromagnetic 'family' or **spectrum**.

The electromagnetic spectrum

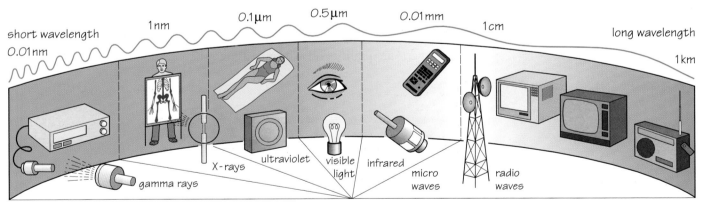

Collect

- Information sheet on electromagnetic waves

Cut out the fact cards and stick them in your book in order of increasing wavelength. Use the picture to help you.

1 Which electromagnetic waves can we detect with our senses?
2 Describe one use that has been found for each type of radiation.
3 Which type of radiation can
    a cause a sun tan   **c** be used to take photographs
    b toast bread   **d** be used for remote control?

Singing in the bath

People enjoy singing in the bathroom because the sound bounces off the walls, giving extra volume and richness to their voices. Sounds are greatly affected by the surroundings. Your singing would sound quite different in a cathedral compared with on a football pitch.

Many musical instruments also use echoes to improve their sound. They bounce their sound waves across air trapped in a box or cavity and produce complicated echoes. These add quality and interest to the sound.

If you clap your hands in a cathedral or a large hall, the sound may take several seconds to die away. The sound sets off in all directions and is reflected by the walls many times over, filling the space with multiple echoes. This is called **reverberation**.

Cathedrals have stone walls that reflect sound well and the echoes take a long time to die away. Concert halls full of people do not reflect the sound so well and have shorter reverberation times. The walls must be carefully designed to give some echo or else the hall sounds 'dead' and heavy.

Reverberation can be added electronically to recorded sounds. Multiple 'reflections' of different strengths and durations are added to the original sound to give it 'atmosphere'. You can often hear this done to voice parts on pop records.

Collect

- Tuning fork
- Small box
- Megaphone
- Guitar
- Scarf
- Mug
- Rubber band

The pictures show some ways to investigate reverberation.

1 Follow the suggestions in the pictures.
2 Listen closely to the difference that the air cavity makes, especially to the tone quality and volume of the note.

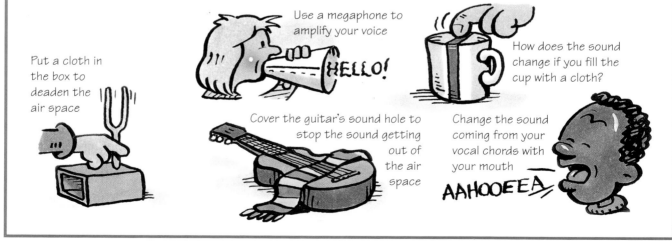

Put a cloth in the box to deaden the air space

Use a megaphone to amplify your voice

HELLO!

How does the sound change if you fill the cup with a cloth?

Cover the guitar's sound hole to stop the sound getting out of the air space

Change the sound coming from your vocal chords with your mouth

AAHOOEEA

 Write an article on *Reverberation*, including observations from some of your own experiments.

Hearing for survival

Bat

Owl

Snake

Whale

The animals above all depend on hearing for their survival. Investigate **one** of these animals (or you can choose a different animal) to find out

- how the animal hears
- its range of audible sound frequencies
- the distance over which it can hear
- why hearing is important for its survival.

 Write a short report or present your findings as a poster.

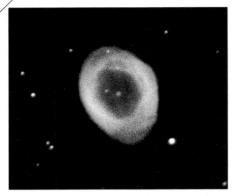

The Ring Nebula, a shell of gas remaining from a nova explosion about 20 000 years ago

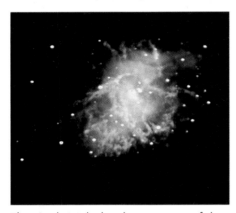

The Crab Nebula, the remnant of the 1054 supernova

A star's life

Astronomers think that a star is born when a huge cloud of gas, mainly hydrogen, is drawn together by gravity. As the volume of the gas cloud gets smaller the gas gets hotter and the pressure within the cloud increases. The atoms of hydrogen at its centre or **core** collide more often. When hydrogen atoms collide hard enough they combine to form helium. This reaction releases energy (as light energy) and the new star shines. Eventually the outward pressure caused by the energy release inside the star balances the inward pull of gravity, and the star stops contracting. It settles down to steadily burn its supply of hydrogen fuel. The star has reached 'middle age'. For a star like our own Sun middle age lasts for about 10 thousand million years.

When all the available hydrogen in the core has turned to helium, the star's middle age is over and it enters 'old age'. Gravity makes its core shrink and get even hotter, but its outer layers swell and cool. The star becomes a **red giant**. What happens next depends on the size of the star.

The core of a medium-sized star, like our Sun, contracts until collisions between helium atoms form atoms of carbon and oxygen. Eventually the helium fuel will also be used up. The star's core will contract again and the outer layers will blow away, perhaps in an explosion or **nova**, leaving the hot core as a **white dwarf**. The white dwarf will very slowly cool, grow faint and die.

The contraction in a larger star may lead to a much greater explosion called a **supernova**, which can shine as brightly as a whole galaxy. In 1054, a new light appeared in the sky that was bright enough to see during the day. It faded after two years, but the remains of this supernova can be seen today as a faint mass of expanding gas called the Crab Nebula. The very dense core left behind (a **neutron star**) spins rapidly and beams out radio waves and is called a **pulsar** (short for **puls**ating st**ar**).

An even larger star may collapse further under the powerful gravity of its own mass to become a **black hole**. It will be very small and have a huge density. The gravitational pull of such a body is so great that even light cannot escape from it.

1 How do stars first form?
2 What fuel is used by a star when it is
   a in middle age   **b** in old age?
3 When the volume of a gas decreases what happens to
   a the temperature   **b** the pressure of the gas?
4 Draw a flow diagram to show the possible life history of a star.
5 If you have a telescope/binoculars, examine the night sky. Look for

   • the Milky Way (a hazy band of stars)
   • star clusters, like the Seven Sisters
   • constellations of stars, using a reference book to help you.

Flat Earth

In earlier times the Earth was thought to be flat. In ancient Greece, Aristotle (384–322 BC) first suggested that it was a sphere. He noticed that the position of the stars shifted as he travelled from north to south, and that during a lunar eclipse the Earth cast a curved shadow on the Moon. A fellow Greek, Eratosthenes (276–194 BC), showed by an experiment that the Earth cannot be flat and at the same time estimated its circumference.

He argued that if the Earth *were* flat and the Sun a long way off, identical vertical sticks would cast shadows of the same length anywhere in the world. He measured such shadows at midday on the same day of the year in two Egyptian cities 800 km apart. They had different lengths, so the Earth cannot be flat.

From the difference he calculated the Earth's circumference to be about 40 000 km, not much more than the correct value.

The Sun is a sphere too. You can estimate its diameter from simple measurements.

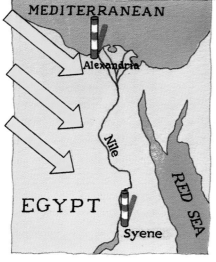

If the Earth were flat, the stick would cast the same length of shadow in Alexandria and Syene

On a curved Earth the Sun may be directly overhead in Syene but not in Alexandria. In Syene the stick casts no shadow but in Alexandria it does

Collect

- Clamp stand
- Ruler
- Drawing pin
- 2 pieces of card
- Tape

1 Draw two parallel lines 5 mm apart on a sheet of card.
2 Make a pinhole in the centre of the second piece of card.
3 Set up the apparatus as shown.

DO NOT LOOK DIRECTLY AT THE SUN.

4 Point the clamp stand at the Sun. A circle of light will fall on to the card on the base.
5 Move the clamp until the circle of light fits exactly between the lines.
6 Measure the distance between the two pieces of card.
7 Calculate the diameter of the Sun using this equation.

$$\text{diameter of Sun (km)} = \frac{\text{diameter of circle (5 mm)} \times \text{distance to Sun (150 000 000 km)}}{\text{distance between pieces of card (mm)}}$$

1 Write a newspaper article describing ancient and modern evidence that proves the Earth is not flat.
2 Draw and label the apparatus for your experiment. Show your calculation for the Sun's diameter.

Shaping the land

The landscape can be shaped slowly

or quickly

Collect

- Poster paper
- Coloured pencils

1 Use either *The landscape can be shaped slowly* or *The landscape can be shaped quickly* as your title. Use the resources in your classroom to find spectacular or unusual, exciting information about your chosen topic. (Use books, CD-ROMs and the Internet if available.)

2 From the information, make up a colourful poster that describes what you have discovered. Your poster should be displayed on the classroom wall when it is finished.

Rock plates

Two hundred million years ago the Earth would have looked quite different from space. Geologists believe there was a single landmass that they have called Pangaea. They think that this land mass broke up and that the pieces moved apart to form the continents and oceans we recognise today. This happened because the Earth's crust is made up of many different pieces called **plates**. These plates continue to move very slowly, so 50 million years from now the continents and oceans will have different shapes.

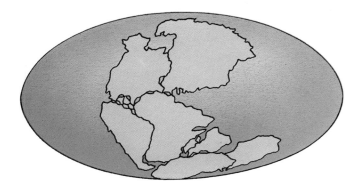

The Earth 200 million years ago

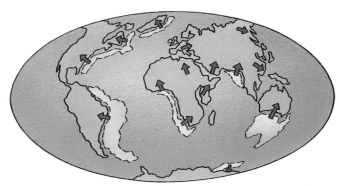

The Earth 50 million years from now

Weak points on the Earth's surface are found where two plates meet. These are zones of active crust where there is a danger of volcanic eruption or of earthquakes.

The earthquake in Kobe, Japan, in 1995 caused a lot of damage

A volcanic eruption

1 How do scientists think the present distribution of continents and oceans came about?
2 Why will the present position of the continents change?
3 Where are zones of active crust found?
   What can happen in these zones?
4 Find out about a recent eruption of a volcano.
   Write a short description of what happened.

Investigating chemical pollution

People change the environment in which they live. These changes should be carefully controlled to protect the environment from damage, otherwise we will all suffer. For example, we burn fuels like coal, oil and natural gas to provide useful heat energy, but we should remember that fuels can cause pollution when they burn. The diagram shows how the fuel that powers a car contributes to environmental damage.

global warming

smog from exhaust

acid rain caused by exhaust gases

carries several people

long distances travelled

lead in exhaust

carries heavy load

speedy movement

waste

LONDON 127 MILES

Collect

- A car pollution card

Each of the investigations on the card will give you information about **one** possible pollutant from a car.

1. Choose an investigation and carry it out. Remember to record your results.
2. Use the books and other resources in the classroom to find out what has been done recently to control this pollutant.
   Key words are: lead-free petrol, catalytic converters, low-burn engines, batteries, solar power, alternative technologies.

Write a short report about your investigation.
Include sentences about the following:

- which pollutant you studied
- its effect on the environment
- the investigation and your results
- what the results showed you
- what has been done recently to overcome this source of pollution
- your own opinion about cars and pollution.

Inheritance

Relatives, especially long-lost relatives, enjoy spotting characteristics that come from one parent or another.

This happens because a gene can have two forms or **alleles**, called **dominant** and **recessive**. For example,

- attached ear lobes are recessive
- free ear lobes are dominant.

Recessive characteristics occur only when both alleles, inherited from each parent, are recessive. Any other combination of alleles produces the dominant form of the characteristic.

Some inherited characteristics are shown below.
Dominant characteristics are labelled in BLACK.
Recessive characteristics are labelled in RED.

This person inherited the recessive allele of a gene from both parents – **homozygous recessive**

This person inherited the dominant allele of a gene from at least one parent. Both alleles dominant – **homozygous dominant**
One allele dominant and one recessive – **heterozygous**

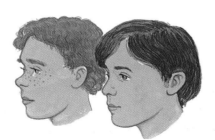

freckles
red hair
long eyelashes
upturned nose

no freckles
non-red hair
short eyelashes
straight nose

widow's peak
straight hair
free ear lobes
brown eyes

straight hair line
curly/kinky hair
attached ear lobes
blue eyes

Collect

- 3 beakers
- 2 different colours of bead
- Coloured pencils
- Family tree sheet

Family tree
Work with a partner to complete the family tree sheet.
Follow the instructions on the sheet.

Girl or boy?

It is possible to discover the sex of an unborn baby. The doctor removes a little of the liquid that surrounds the baby in the womb. Cells in this liquid are examined with a microscope. Thread-like structures can be seen in the nucleus. These are **chromosomes**. A single chromosome is made up of thousands of genes.

Chromosomes in the nucleus of a *Drosophila* (fruit fly) cell

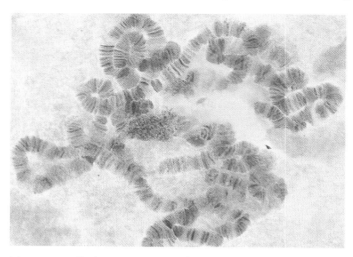

Human cells have 23 matching pairs of chromosomes, making 46 in all. One of each pair is inherited from each parent. The chromosome sets shown have been made by cutting up photographs of two cell nuclei. The final two chromosomes are the sex chromosomes. They control the sex of the baby.

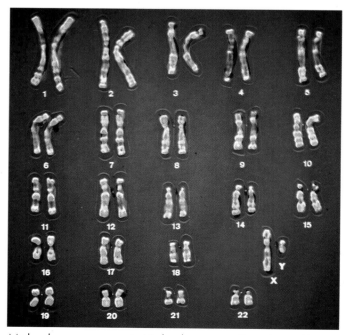

Male chromosome set. Males have one X and one Y sex chromosome

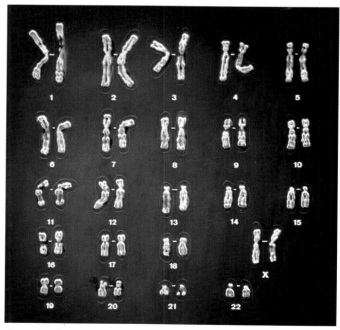

Female chromosome set. Females have two X sex chromosomes

When sex cells are produced they carry only one chromosome of each pair. As a result each sex cell has one sex chromosome only.

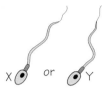

There are two types of sperm cell

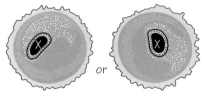

There is only one type of egg cell

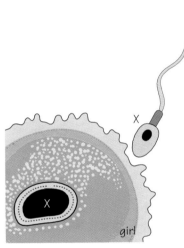

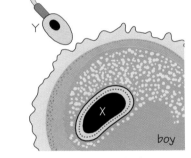

At conception there is a roughly equal chance of a male or female baby being produced.

Collect

- Colour-blind test cards

The gene for colour-blindness is recessive and is on the X-chromosome.

Test boys and girls for colour-blindness. Keep a record of the results.

1 What are sex chromosomes?

2 Which sex chromosomes are carried by

- females
- males?

3 Use diagrams to explain why you would expect equal numbers of girls and boys to be born.

4 Why would you expect more boys than girls to be colour-blind?

Moving designs

Two sets of muscles act against each other to make bones at a joint move. This is true in all animals with joints. The muscle that lifts the footballer's lower leg is shown in green and the muscle that straightens the leg is shown in red.

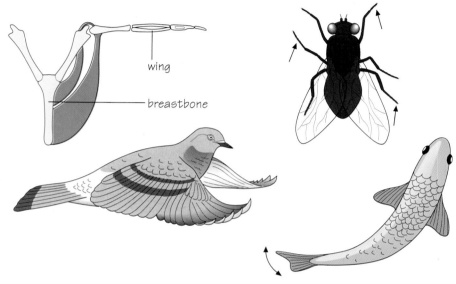

wing

breastbone

Flick a tail
Fish swim by flicking their tails from side to side.

Shake a leg
Insect legs have joints that move when they walk. But, their skeleton is on the outside and their muscles are on the inside!

Flap a wing
Birds fly by flapping their wings. The diagram above shows the skeleton from the front. Both muscles are attached at one end to the large breastbone.

Collect

- Movement worksheet
- Red and green crayons

1 Complete the drawing on the worksheet of the fish to show the muscle used to flick the tail to the right (in red), and the muscle used to move the tail to the left (in green). (The ✖s give you a clue about where the muscles join the bone.)
2 Complete the drawing on the worksheet of the insect leg to show the muscle used to bend the leg (in red), and the muscle used to straighten the leg (in green).
3 Complete the drawing on the worksheet of the bird skeleton. Draw the muscle that would lower the wing in red. Draw the muscle that would raise the wing in green.
4 Label all the muscles you have marked. Stick the worksheet into your book.

It's the way you say it

Human beings are social animals. We can communicate with one another by speaking and listening, and by reading and writing. Four forms of communication that use signs, sounds or signals are shown below.

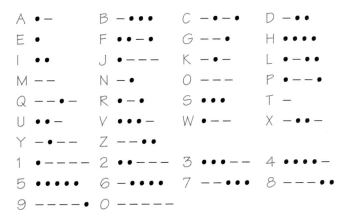

A •–	B –•••	C –•–•	D –••
E •	F ••–•	G ––•	H ••••
I ••	J •–––	K –•–	L •–••
M ––	N –•	O –––	P •––•
Q ––•–	R •–•	S •••	T –
U ••–	V •••–	W •––	X –••–
Y –•––	Z ––••		
1 •––––	2 ••–––	3 •••––	4 ••••–
5 •••••	6 –••••	7 ––•••	8 –––••
9 ––––•	0 –––––		

Morse code alphabet

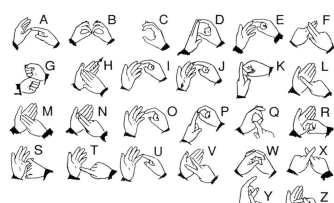

Sign language alphabet

Road signs/symbols

Braille alphabet

Collect

- Pin
- Coloured pencils

1 Write your name in Morse and in Braille (push the pin through the paper from the other side to make raised dots). Try it in sign language.

2 Communicate the name of your three favourite colours to a partner by

- tapping out Morse for colour 1
- signing the word for colour 2
- writing colour 3 in Braille.

Now discover the colours your partner likes best.

3 Design two signs without words that would communicate **two** of the ideas below. Use colour carefully.

- electric car
- hot surface

- danger, acid rain
- danger, noise pollution.

Drawing atoms

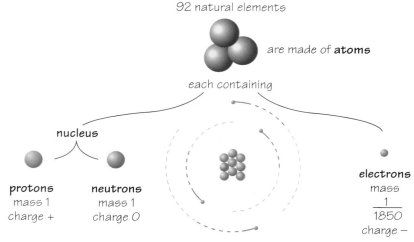

92 natural elements

are made of **atoms**

each containing

nucleus

protons
mass 1
charge +

neutrons
mass 1
charge 0

electrons
mass
$\frac{1}{1850}$
charge −

mass number
gives the number of protons plus neutrons

overall charge
allows the number of electrons to be calculated (*We will not use this yet.*)

7

Li⁺

3

atomic number
gives the number of protons

symbol
identifies the type of atom, and enables you to look up its atomic number

Our ideas can be summarised like this

All atoms contain the same ingredients: protons, neutrons and electrons. Different atoms must be different inside in some way. Presumably, atoms of lithium contain a different mixture of ingredients than atoms of beryllium. An atom can be described using a symbol and numbers.

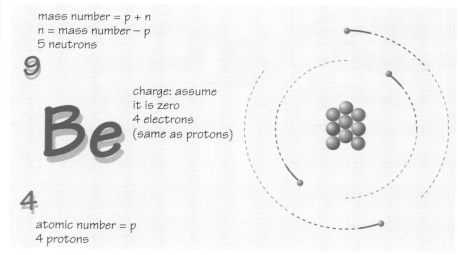

mass number = p + n
n = mass number − p
5 neutrons

9

Be

4

charge: assume it is zero
4 electrons
(same as protons)

atomic number = p
4 protons

If you know the numbers you can draw a picture of the atom. Write the title *Particles in an atom* in your book. Make notes including these key points

- Mass number
- Atomic number
- Symbol.

Give examples each time.

Draw and label ^{12}C, ^{16}O, ^{19}F and ^{23}Na.

Spot the family

By the late eighteenth century, people were trying to find a pattern in the behaviour of the elements. In 1869, a Russian called Dmitri Mendeleev produced the first version of the Periodic Table. You are going to try to follow the kind of thinking that he had to use.

Collect

- Element cards
- Card grid

1 Read the element descriptions on all the cards.
2 Divide the cards into eight groups, with three similar cards in each group.

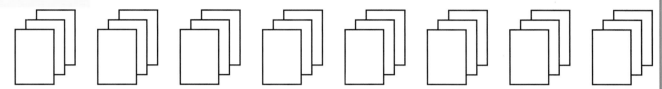

3 If you have managed this step correctly then one of the cards in each group will be marked with a letter as well as a number, e.g. A3, B4.

4 Put these marked cards on the grid.

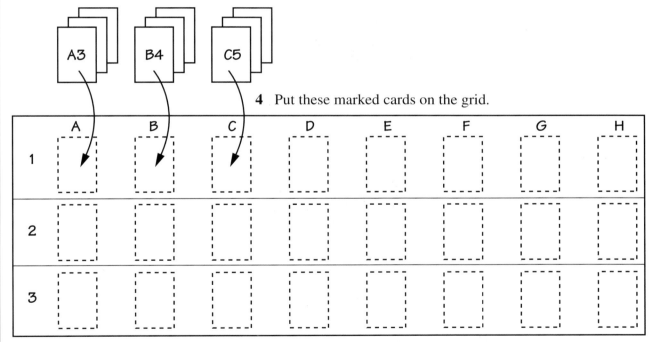

5 Can you work out where the other cards go? Try it.
6 Check your answer by looking up the identity of each card and then comparing your grid with the Periodic Table.

1 Explain how you grouped the cards.
2 **a** What does the number on each card represent?
  b What would be the number of the next card on the grid?
3 One of the cards has no description of the element. Predict what this description might say.

Valency and the Periodic Table

The drawing below shows the valency cards of the first 20 elements. Use this drawing and the Periodic Table to find a pattern in the valency numbers.

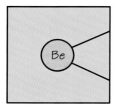 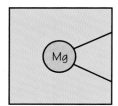 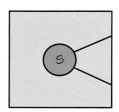 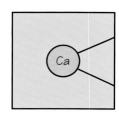 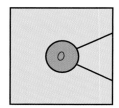

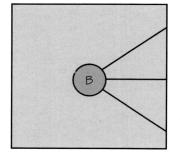 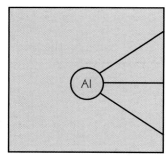 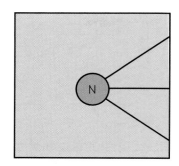 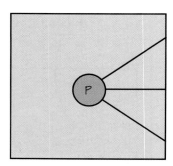

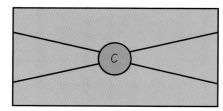 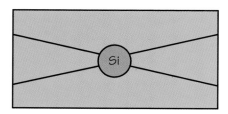

1 Describe the pattern that connects the valency number and the arrangement of atoms in the Periodic Table.

2 Use this pattern to work out the valency picture and formulae of

- caesium chloride
- barium chloride
- strontium telluride
- gallium iodide
- rubidium selenide.

Electricity from metals

An electric current is a flow of electrons. During chemical reactions, some substances will transfer electrons from their atoms to the atoms of the other reactant. This is how a chemical battery works.

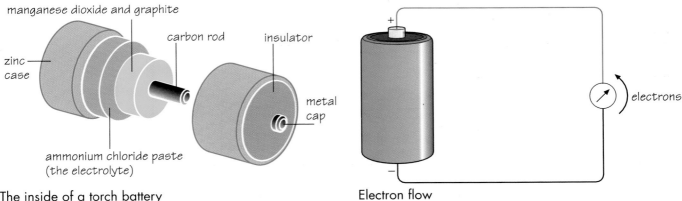

The inside of a torch battery

Electron flow

When a metal reacts with water its atoms lose electrons. The more reactive the metal, the greater the number of atoms losing their electrons in a given time.

Less reactive

More reactive

Collect

- A data sheet
- Components for the circuit
- Zinc
- Copper
- Iron
- Magnesium
- Tin
- Lead

Set up this electrical cell.

a Read the voltmeter and write down the voltage on your data sheet.

b Swap the zinc for a piece of iron. Note the voltage on the sheet again.

Refer to the reactivity series and predict the missing voltage values on the data sheet. Record your predictions then check them by experiment.

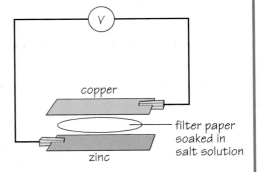

1 Write a report of your experiment.
2 Why is a pattern like the reactivity series useful?
3 Look at the reactivity series of metals and explain why
   a rings and bracelets are made from metals at the bottom rather than the top of the series
   b water pipes are made from copper rather than magnesium
   c ships containing a large amount of aluminium burn fiercely
   d hydrochloric acid can be safely used to clean copper but not to clean sodium.

Types of compounds

There are two main types of compounds – **ionic** and **covalent**.

1 Ionic compounds are those that contain ions. An ionic compound is usually made from a metal joined to a non-metal. **Collect** and examine a model of an ionic lattice.

The **metal** ion is **positive**

The other ion is **negative**

The ions have opposite charges: they are strongly **attracted**. They form a huge network called an **ionic lattice**. This network is very **strong**

However, the lattice can be **broken down** by lots of heat or water. The charged ions become **free** to move. The substance will now conduct electricity

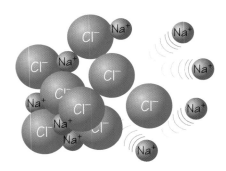

2 Covalent compounds do not contain ions. A covalent compound is usually made from two or more non-metals joined together. **Collect** and examine a model of a covalent molecule.

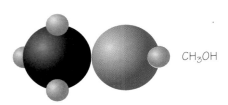

CH_3OH

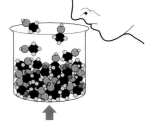

Covalent compounds often contain small uncharged **molecules**. Each molecule is strongly bonded. However, molecules are not strongly attracted to their neighbours

As the molecules are not strongly attracted, they can be **separated easily** by **a little** heat and sometimes by water. However, without charged particles, the substance cannot conduct electricity

Collect

- Set of solutions
- Bulb or ammeter
- Power supply (set at 4 V d.c.)
- 3 connecting wires
- 2 crocodile clips

1 Set up this circuit.

2 Use the circuit to discover which solutions contain ionic and which ones contain covalent compounds (if you do not know what to do then re-read the text above). Record your results.

3 Collect a formulae card and check your results (refer to the Periodic Table to work out whether a compound is ionic or covalent).

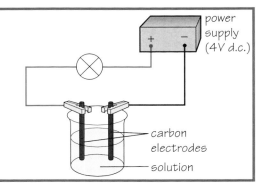

power supply (4V d.c.)

carbon electrodes

solution

 Write a short summary of the differences between the two types of compounds (you can look for more information in the resources available).

Survey of animal breeds

You were asked in an earlier unit to find out about the ancestral parents of present-day cats and dogs (see page 66). When animals are bred in captivity certain features can be selected. To increase the hair length of a dog, just select the longest-haired puppy to be a parent for the next generation. Then choose the longest-haired dogs from that generation to produce the next and so on. Over many years, the dogs' hair will become longer and longer.

For example this sheep

this one

and this one

has been bred for meat

to survive harsh conditions

for its wool

1 Design a survey of people's pets (dogs/cats) – to find out *either* which breeds are most common – this will be a survey of **facts** *or* which features people like/dislike about particular breeds – this will be a survey of **opinions**.

You will have to think about methods of surveying, what questions to ask, size of sample (how many people to ask), and ways of recording people's views.

2 Carry out the survey. Record the answers.

You will have to think about when and where to carry out your survey, whether you need some help and how much time the exercise is likely to take.

3 Present your results to the class.

You will have to think about what your results mean. You will also have to think about ways of presenting facts or opinions so that you make an impact on your audience.

4 Write a paragraph about how your survey could be improved.

You will have to think about your methods and results critically. How could you have been more precise? Is there any way that you could test your conclusions?

Polymers

The small molecules (called **monomers**) in crude oil can be joined together like beads in a necklace. They become part of a big molecule called a **polymer**.

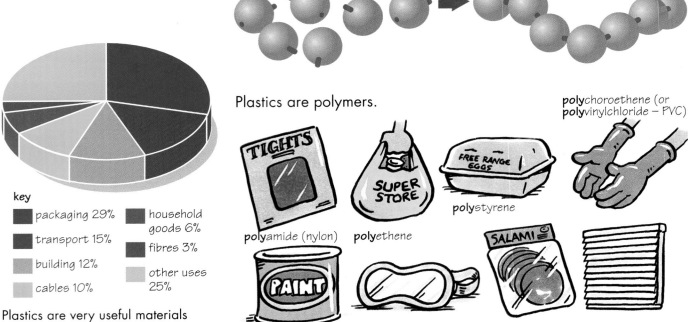

Plastics are polymers.

polyamide (nylon)   polyethene   polystyrene   **poly**choroethene (or **poly**vinylchloride – PVC)

polyurethane   polycarbonate   polypropene   polyphenylene

The name of the plastic often indicates that the substance is a polymer.

key

■ packaging 29%
■ transport 15%
■ building 12%
■ cables 10%
■ household goods 6%
■ fibres 3%
■ other uses 25%

Plastics are very useful materials

Collect

- A polymer card
- Safety glasses

1 Read the card. Make a list of all the equipment and substances that you will need.
2 Collect the things on your list.
3 Follow the instructions on the card and make the polymer.

 For each material that you make, write out a report like the one below.

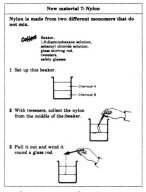

Polymer card

Your report

A quantitative study of energy efficiency

The electrical potential energy from a battery can be calculated by using a formula.

The amount of heat energy absorbed by water can also be calculated by using a different formula.

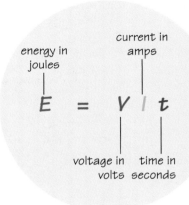

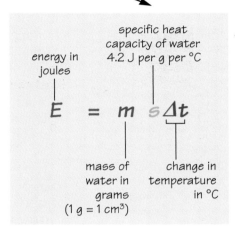

It should therefore be possible to use an electrically powered heater to heat up some water, make certain key measurements during the process, and then calculate the energy put into the heater and the energy transferred to the water. These two quantities will enable the efficiency of the heater to be calculated.

---

1 Examine the circuit diagram.
Collect the apparatus you require and build the circuit.

2 To measure the energy input you will have to record

- the voltage
- the current
- the time (in seconds) that the heater is switched on.

Arrange to make and record these measurements.

3 To measure the energy output you will have to record

- the specific heat capacity of water, which is in the data book
- the mass of water used (1g = 1cm^3)
- the temperature change during the heating process.

Arrange to make and record these measurements.

4 To calculate the efficiency of the heater you will have to apply the formula above.

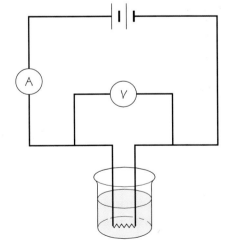

 Write a full report for your experiment.
Include a description of method, a table of results, all your calculations and a conclusion that states your value for the efficiency of the heater. Think about and write down any ways that the accuracy of your work could be improved.

Index